AZEOTROPIC DATA—II

Compiled by LEE H. HORSLEY
The Dow Chemical Co.
Midland, Mich.

With the cooperation of WILLIAM S. TAMPLIN
Union Carbide Chemicals Co.
South Charleston, W. Va.

Number 35

ADVANCES IN CHEMISTRY SERIES

American Chemical Society

Washington, D. C.

1962

Copyright © 1962

AMERICAN CHEMICAL SOCIETY

All Rights Reserved

Library of Congress Catalog Card 52-3085

PRINTED IN THE UNITED STATES OF AMERICA

ADVANCES IN CHEMISTRY SERIES

Robert F. Gould, Editor

AMERICAN CHEMICAL SOCIETY APPLIED PUBLICATIONS

CONTENTS

INTRODUCTION

This volume is a supplement to "Azeotropic Data" published as ADVANCES IN CHEMISTRY SERIES No. 6, American Chemical Society (1952).

It includes revised data on systems in the original table plus new data on azeotropes, nonazeotropes, and vapor-liquid equilibria collected since 1952. No attempt has been made to evaluate the data. Where appreciable differences occur in data from different sources, more than one set of data is recorded. Where minor differences occur, only one set of data is recorded, but all references are cited.

A brief description is included for calculating azeotropic data for immiscible systems from vapor pressure data.

In general data have been obtained from the original literature. Where the original literature was not available, data have been taken from *Chemical Abstracts*. In a few instances, data have been taken from collections of azeotropic data in handbooks, review articles, and so forth.

Acknowledgment is made to Commercial Solvents Corp., The Dow Chemical Co., Eastman Chemical Products Inc., Farbenwerke Hoechst, Imperial Chemical Industries Limited, Minnesota Mining and Manufacturing Co., and Union Carbide Chemicals Co. for supplying unpublished data for inclusion in the tables.

The tables are arranged in the same manner as the previous volume. This is based on empirical formula as in *Chemical Abstracts* except that all inorganic compounds are listed first, alphabetically by empirical formula.

For a given binary system the lower order component according to empirical formula is chosen as the A-component and under each A-component the B-components are also arranged according to empirical formula. For ternary and quarternary systems the same arrangement is used, using the lowest order formula as A-component, the next lowest order as B-component, and so on.

With a few exceptions for common chemical names, nomenclature in the tables follows the *Chemical Abstracts* nomenclature system.

Abbreviations

max. b.p.	Maximum boiling point azeotrope (negative azeotrope)
min. b.p.	Minimum boiling point azeotrope (positive azeotrope)
atm.	Pressure in standard atmospheres
mm.	Pressure in millimeters of Hg
p.s.i.a.	Pressure in pounds per square inch absolute
p.s.i.g.	Pressure in pounds per square inch gage
v-l.	Vapor-liquid equilibrium data are given in the original reference
v.p.	Vapor pressure
vol. %	Azeotropic concentration is given in volume per cent. Unless so indicated, all concentration data are in weight %
~	Approximate
>, <	Greater than, less than

Corrections for Azeotropic Data—I

The following errors appeared in "Azeotropic Data," ADVANCES IN CHEMISTRY SERIES No. 6.

Page	System	
4	65	Replace A-component, thionyl chloride, with sulfuryl chloride.
6	131	Azeotropic composition is 7.9 wt. %. This is an error in the original reference.
7	176	Formula should be $C_3H_7NO_3$.
8	240	Replace 57% with 43% for azeotropic composition.
9	281	This system should follow system 277.
10	306	Replace "cyclohexane" with "cyclohexene."
13	482	Replace 6.32 by -6.32 for b.p. of methylamine.
19	834–835	A-component formula is $CHBr_3$.
23	1059–1060	Between systems 1059 and 1060 insert: $A = CH_2I_2$ Diiodomethane b. 181°C.
28	1389	Replace 59.05 with 49.05 for azeotropic b.p.
33	1696	A-component formula is C_2HBrCl_2.
83	4708–4709	Replace 43.6 with 38 for A-component b.p.
114	6546	Replace 11 with 154.5 for azeotropic b.p.
123		Between system 7090 and 7091, omit: $A = C_4H_9I$ 1-Iodo-2-methyl propane.
149	8651	Replace reference 244 with 243.
154	8920	Replace $C_7H_{16}O_4$, 2-[2-(2-methoxyethoxy)ethoxy]-ethanol, with $C_6H_{14}O_3$, 2-(2-ethoxyethoxy)ethanol, and insert after system 8909.
251	14519	% B-component should be 93.4%.
257	14658	% A-component should be 8.5%.
267		Formula Cl_2O_2S. Replace thionyl chloride with sulfuryl chloride.
284		Under $C_6H_6O_2$, pyrocatechol, replace system 3510 with 3570.
296		Formula C_8H_{18}. Replace 3-ethylheptane with 3-methyl-heptane.

Calculation of Azeotropic Data for Immiscible Systems

There are many binary heterogeneous azeotropes which are not listed in the literature because the azeotropic data can readily be calculated from the vapor pressure data of the components.

For a mixture of two completely immiscible liquids the total vapor pressure is equal to the sum of the vapor pressures of the two components at a given temperature. Therefore, from a plot of the vapor pressures of the two components, it is possible to determine the temperature at which the sum of the vapor pressures is equal to 760 mm. This temperature is the azeotropic boiling point of the system at 760 mm. The boiling point at any other pressure can be obtained in a similar manner.

Further, the azeotropic composition can be calculated from the expression

$$\text{Mole } \% \ A = \frac{V_A \times 100}{V_A + V_B}$$

V_A = vapor pressure of component A
V_B = vapor pressure of component B

Table I. Binary Systems

		B-Component		Azeotropic Data			
No.	Formula	Name	B.P.,°C.	B.P.,°C.	Wt.%A		Ref.
A =	A	Argon	-186				
1	O₂	Oxygen	-183	Nonazeotrope		v-l	71
		1-15 atm.	...	...	...	v-l	232
		90°-96° K.	...	...	...	v-l	340
2	C₅F₁₂	Perfluoropentane, 25°C.	...	Nonazeotrope		v-l	237
A =	AsCl₃	Arsenic Chloride	130				
3	GeCl₄	Germanium chloride	86.5	Nonazeotrope		v-l	298
A =	BeF₂	Beryllium Fluoride					
4	FNa	Sodium fluoride,					
		509°-1061° C.	...			v-l	299
A =	B₂H₆	Diborane					
5	C₄H₁₀O	Ethyl ether,					
		25-100 p.s.i.g.	...	Nonazeotrope		v-l	206
A =	BrF₃	Bromine Trifluoride	135				
6	BrF₅	Bromine pentafluoride	...	Nonazeotrope		v-l	200
7	Br₂	Bromine, 1760 mm.	...	75	84.4	v-l	101
		" 3800 mm.	...	100	81.5	v-l	101
8	FH	Hydrogen fluoride	19.4	Azeotropic			91
9	F₆U	Uranium hexafluoride	56	Nonazeotrope			91
A =	BrF₅	Bromine Pentafluoride					
10	FH	Hydrogen fluoride	19.4	20	56		4,91
		" 4 atm.	...	...	79		91
11	F₆U	Uranium hexafluoride	56	Min. b.p.	82		91
		" 3 atm.	...	Nonazeotrope		v-l	203
		" 70°	...	Nonazeotrope		v-l	203
		" 90°	...	Nonazeotrope		v-l	203
		" 100 p.s.i.a.	...	...	62.5		91
A =	Br₂	Bromine	58.9				
12	FH	Hydrogen fluoride	19.4	Azeotropic			91
13	F₆U	Uranium hexafluoride	56	Azeotropic			91
14	CCl₄	Carbon tetrachloride,					
		736 mm.	76	57.7	89.1	v-l	311
15	C₂Cl₃F₃	1,1,2-Trichloro-1,2, 2-trifluoroethane	47.6	41	40.8	v-l	312
16	C₂Cl₄F₂	1,1,1,2-Tetrachloro- 2,2-difluoroethane	91.6	57.8	89.5	v-l	312
17	C₂HCl₃F₂	1,2,2-Trichloro-1,1- difluoroethane, 736 mm.	71.1	54.1	73.5	v-l	313
18	C₂H₂Cl₂F₂	1,1-Dichloro-2,2- difluoroethane, 735 mm.	59	49.6	62	v-l	313
19	C₃Cl₃F₅	1,2,2-Trichloro-1,1, 3,3,3-pentafluoro- propane	72.5	49.1	60.5	v-l	312
20	C₇H₅F₃	α, α, α-Trifluorotoluene	103.9	58.1	97	v-l	312
A =	Br₃P	Phosphorus Tribromide	175.3				
21	CₙH₂ₙ₊₂	Paraffin hydrocarbons	...	Min. b.p.			234

		B-Component		Azeotropic Data		
No.	Formula	Name	B.P.,°C.	B.P.,°C.	Wt.%A	Ref.
A =	CO_2	**Carbon Dioxide**	**-78.5**			
22	H_2S	Hydrogen sulfide,				
		20-80 atm.	-59.6	Nonazeotrope	v-1	16, 17
23	N_2O	Nitrous oxide	-90.7	Min. b.p.	v-1	293
24	C_2H_2	Acetylene	-84	Nonazeotrope	v-1	293
		" Crit. press.	...	Nonazeotrope	v-1	293
25	C_2H_4	Ethylene, <4 atm.	...	Nonazeotrope	v-1	293
		" 12 atm.	...	...	28.9 v-1	293
		" Crit. press.	...	...	51 v-1	293
26	C_2H_6	Ethane	-88.6	...	59.5 v-1	293
		" Crit. press.	...	...	77.5 v-1	293
A =	ClF_3	**Chlorine Trifluoride**				
27	ClH	Hydrogen chloride	-85	Reacts		4
28	FH	Hydrogen fluoride	19.4	Azeotropic		91
		" 1183 mm.	...	20	93 v-1	90
		" 90 p.s.i.g.	...	...	94.5	91
		" 125 p.s.i.g.	...	...	94	91
		" 143 p.s.i.g.	...	...	93.8	91
		" 148 p.s.i.g.	...	...	93.7	91
29	F_6U	Uranium hexafluoride	56	Nonazeotrope	v-1	89, 91
A =	ClH	**Hydrogen Chloride**	**-85**			
30	Cl_2	Chlorine, 350 mm.	-44	Nonazeotrope		4
31	H_2O	Water, 100 p.s.i.g.	169	177	85.2	334
		" 520 p.s.i.g.	244	250	93.5	334
		" 860 p.s.i.g.	275	280	97.2	334
		" 1360 p.s.i.g.	306	310	99.4	334
		" 1815 p.s.i.g.	328	330	99.9	334
32	CH_4O	Methanol	64.7	Max. b.p.		76
A =	Cl_2	**Chlorine**	**-34.6**			
33	FH	Hydrogen fluoride,				
		350 mm.	3.0	-47	92	4
		"	19.4	-35	...	4
A =	Cl_2SO_2	**Sulfuryl Chloride**	**69.1**			
34	CCl_4	Carbon tetrachloride	76.75	Nonazeotrope	v-1	338
35	C_2Cl_6	Hexachloroethane	184.8	Nonazeotrope	v-1	338
36	$C_2H_2Cl_4$	1,1,2,2,-Tetra-chloroethane	146.2	Nonazeotrope	v-1	338
37	$C_2H_4Cl_2$	1,2-Dichloroethane	83.45	Nonazeotrope	v-1	338
A =	Cl_3HSi	**Trichlorosilane**				
38	C_6H_6	Benzene, 30°-40° C.	...	Nonazeotrope, v.p. curve		302
A =	Cl_3P	**Phosphorus Trichloride**	**76**			
39	C_6H_{12}	Cyclohexane	80.75	Nonazeotrope		236
40	C_6H_{14}	Hexane	68.8	68.7	8 vol. %	234
41	C_7H_{16}	2,2-Dimethylpentane	79.1	Min. b.p.		234, 236
42	C_7H_{16}	2,3-Dimethylpentane	89.8	74.5	98.8 vol.%	234
43	C_7H_{16}	2,4-Dimethylpentane	80.5	74.2	73	234
44	C_7H_{16}	2,2,3-Trimethylbutane	80.9	74.5	77	234
A =	Cl_4Si	**Silicon Tetrachloride**	**57.6**			
45	CH_3SiCl_3	Methyl trichloro-silane, 20°-66°	...	Nonazeotrope, v.p. curve		179
46	CH_4SiCl_2	Methyl dichloro-silane, 20°-66°	...	Nonazeotrope, v.p. curve		179
A =	Cl_4Sn	**Tin Chloride**	**114.1**			
47	CCl_4	Carbon tetrachloride	76.8	Nonazeotrope	v-1	34
48	C_8H_{18}	n-Octane	125.7	Nonazeotrope	v-1	34

TABLE I   BINARY SYSTEMS   **7**

		B-Component		Azeotropic Data		
No.	Formula	Name	B.P.,°C.	B.P.,°C.	Wt.%A	Ref.

A =	Cl_4Ti	**Titanium Tetrachloride**	**146.2**			
49	C_2Cl_4O	Trichloroacetyl				
		chloride	118	Nonazeotrope	v-l	300
50	$C_2H_2Cl_2O$	Chloroacetyl chloride	105	Nonazeotrope	v-l	300
51	$C_2H_2Cl_4$	1,1,2,2-Tetrachloro-				
		ethane, 740 mm.	136.6	135.4 91.7	v-l	32
A =	DH	**Deuterium Hydride**	–			
52	D_2	Deuterium, 18°-28° K.	-249.7	Nonazeotrope	v-l	238
53	H_2	Hydrogen, 18°-28° K.	-252.7	Nonazeotrope	v-l	238
A =	D_2	**Deuterium**	**-249.7**			
54	H_2	Hydrogen, 18°-28° K.	-252.7	Nonazeotrope	v-l	238
A =	FH	**Hydrogen Fluoride**	**19.4**			
55	F_5Sb	Antimony pentafluoride	142.7	Nonazeotrope	v-l	301
56	F_6U	Uranium hexafluoride				
		" 85 p.s.i.g.	...	... 22		91
		" 110 p.s.i.g.	...	... 18		91
		" 132 p.s.i.g.	...	... 15		91
		" 145 p.s.i.g.	...	... 14		91
57	CCl_2F_2	Dichlorodifluoromethane,				
		150 p.s.i.g.	48	39 7.5		334
58	$CHClF_2$	Chlorodifluoromethane				
		" 70 p.s.i.g.	7	<7 3		334
		" 150 p.s.i.g.	29	24 2.7		334
		" 230 p.s.i.g.	45	36 2.8		334
59	$C_2HF_3O_2$	Trifluoroacetic acid		Nonazeotrope	v-l	222
A =	F_6S	**Sulfur Hexafluoride**				
60	C_5F_{12}	Perfluoropentane, 25°C.	–	Nonazeotrope	v-l	237
A =	F_6W	**Tungsten Hexafluoride**	**25/1019; 45/1982 mm.**			
61	C_5F_{10}	Perfluorocyclo-				
		pentane	25/833	25/1035 85.4	v-l	288
		"	45/1642	45/2010 83.4	v-l	288
62	C_5F_{12}	Perfluoropentane,				
		1140 mm.	40.86	28.11 93.2	v-l	13
A =	HNO_3	**Nitric Acid**	**86**			
63	H_2O	Water, 50 mm.	37	57.8 13.7	v-l	19
		" 100 mm.	51.6	72.4 13.8	v-l	19
		" 200 mm.	66.5	86.4 14.0	v-l	19
		" 400 mm.	83.0	103.2 14.2	v-l	19
		" 760 mm.	100	120.7 14.4	v-l	19
				See also H_2O-N_2O_5 below		
64	$CHCl_3$	Chloroform	61	47.5 15		258
A =	H_2O	**Water**	**100**			
65	H_2O_2	Hydrogen peroxide	...		v-l	104
66	H_2SO_4	Hydrogen sulfate	...	330 1.7		334
		" 200 mm.	...	... 1.6		334
67	H_4N_2	Hydrazine,				
		124.8 mm.	66.8	74.2 33.2	v-l	30
		" 281.8 mm.	86.5	93.3 32.3	v-l	30
		" 411.2 mm.	96.8	103.6 31.0	v-l	30
		" 560.4 mm.	105.2	111.3 31.4	v-l	30
		" 700.6 mm.	111.7	117.6 32.6	v-l	30
		" 760 mm.	113.8	120 32.3	v-l	30
68	N_2O_5	Nitrogen pentoxide	...	Max. b.p. 40	v-l	199
		"	...	Min. b.p. 14.3		199
		"	...	Max. b.p. 12.5		199
69	CS_2	Carbon disulfide	46.5	43.6 2		334
70	$CHCl_3$	Chloroform	61	56.1 2.8		56
71	CH_2O_2	Formic acid, 40-760 mm.	...	... ...	v-l	42
		"	100.75	107.65 25.5	v-l	56, 217, 360

		B-Component		Azeotropic Data		
No.	Formula	Name	B.P.,°C.	B.P.,°C.	Wt.%A	Ref.
A =	H₂O	Water (continued)	100			
72	CH₃NO₂	Nitromethane	101.2	83.59	23.6	54, 55
73	CH₄O	Methanol	64.7	Nonazeotrope	v-1	68
74	C₂Cl₃F₃	1,1,2-Trichlorotri-fluoroethane	47.5	44.5	1.0	334
75	C₂Cl₄	Tetrachloroethylene	121	88.5	17.2	334
		"	121	87.7	15.8	170
76	C₂HF₃O₂	Trifluoroacetic acid	...	105	21	222
77	C₂H₃Cl₂NO₂	Methyl N,N-dichlo-rocarbamate	...	93	50 vol. %	39
78	C₂H₃Cl₃	1,1,2-Trichloro-ethane	113.8	86.0	16.4	334
79	C₂H₃N	Acetonitrile, 10 mm.	-15	<-16	2.6	336
		" 50 mm.	13	<12	5.8	336
		" 760 mm.	80.1	76.5	16.3	336
80	C₂H₄Cl₂	1,2-Dichloroethane	83.5	71.6	8.2	334
			...	75.5	8.2	55
		" 150 mm.	...	33.5	4.9	55
		" 75 mm.	...	19.0	4.9	55
81	C₂H₄O₂	Acetic acid	118.1	Nonazeotrope	v-1	56
82	C₂H₅BrO	2-Bromoethanol, 150 mm.	100	58	55.7	76
83	C₂H₅ClO	2-Chloroethanol, 50 mm.	60	37.1	60.2	334
		" 100 mm.	75	51.1	59.3	334
84	C₂H₅NO₂	Nitroethane	114.07	87.22	28.5	54, 55
85	C₂H₆O	Ethyl alcohol, 150°-350° C.	...	...	...	v-1 14
		" 250-2500 mm.	...	...	...	v-1 251
86	C₂H₆O₂	Ethylene glycol, 76-760 mm.	...	Nonazeotrope	v-1	60
87	C₂H₇NO	2-Aminoethanol	170.5	Nonazeotrope		334
		" 100 mm.	112	Nonazeotrope		334
88	C₂H₈N₂	1,1-Dimethylhydra-zine, 102 mm.	...	Max. b.p. 82.5		37
		"		Nonazeotrope		37
89	C₂H₈N₂	1,2-Ethylenediamine	116	...	18.0	v-1 76
		" >3400 mm.	...	Nonazeotrope		76
		"	116.9	119	18.4	334
90	C₃HF₅O₂	Pentafluoropropionic acid	...	109	10	222
91	C₃H₃N	Acrylonitrile	77.2	70.6	14.3	334
92	C₃H₃NS	Thiazole, 695.5 mm.	...	90	34.8	v-1 219
		" 750 mm.	111.5	92.1	35.3	v-1 219
93	C₃H₄O	Acrolein	52.8	52.4	2.6	334
94	C₃H₄O	2-Propyn-1-ol	115	97	54.5	95
95	C₃H₄O₂	Acrylic acid	141.2	Nonazeotrope		334
96	C₃H₄O₃	Ethylene carbonate	...	Nonazeotrope		334
97	C₃H₅Cl	3-Chloropropene	44.9	43.0	2.2	334
98	C₃H₅Cl	Methylvinyl chloride	...	33	0.9	334
99	C₃H₅NO	Hydracrylonitrile	229.7	Nonazeotrope		334
100	C₃H₆Cl₂O	2,3-Dichloro-1-propanol	183.8	99.4	87	334
101	C₃H₆O	Acetone	56.1	Nonazeotrope	v-1	254
		" 50 p.s.i.a.	...	Nonazeotrope	v-1	254
		" 100 p.s.i.a.	...	125.4	5.2	v-1 254
		" 200 p.s.i.a.	...	157.6	7.2	v-1 254
		" 250 p.s.i.a.	...	168.4	9.4	v-1 254
		" 500 p.s.i.a.	...	206.0	14.3	v-1 254
102	C₃H₆O	Allyl alcohol, 752 mm.	96.90	...	...	v-1 130
103	C₃H₆O	Propionaldehyde	47.9	47.5	2	334
		"	...	47.5	2.5	84
104	C₃H₆O	Propylene oxide	35	Nonazeotrope	v-1	60
105	C₃H₆O₂	1,3-Dioxolane	75.6	71.9	7	334
106	C₃H₆O₂	Ethyl formate	54.2	52.6	5	334

TABLE I   BINARY SYSTEMS   9

No.	Formula	B-Component Name	B.P.,°C.	Azeotropic Data B.P.,°C.	Wt.%A	Ref.
A =	H₂O	**Water (continued)**	**100**			
107	C₃H₆O₂	2-Methoxyacetalde-hyde, 770 mm.	92	88.5	12.8	77
108	C₃H₆O₂	Methyl acetate, <10 p.s.i.a.	...	Nonazeotrope		131
		"	56.3	56.1	5	334
		" 265 mm.	30	30	1.5	334
109	C₃H₇Cl	1-Chloropropane	46.6	44	2.2	334
110	C₃H₇Cl	2-Chloropropane	36.5	35.0	1	334
111	C₃H₇NO	Dimethylformamide, 500 mm.	138	Nonazeotrope		334
		" 200-760 mm.	...	Nonazeotrope	v-l	319
112	C₃H₇NO₂	1-Nitropropane	131.18	91.63	36.5	54, 55
113	C₃H₇NO₂	2-Nitropropane	120.25	88.55	29.4	54, 55
114	C₃H₈O	Propyl alcohol, 47 mm.	...	...	31.8	117
		" 200 mm.	...	56.68	29.6	v-l 228, 306
		" 400 mm.	...	71.92	29.0	v-l 306
		" 600 mm.	...	81.68	28.5	v-l 306
		"		87.65	28.3	v-l 306
		"	In 1.5M CaCl₂ Solution		v-l	72
115	C₃H₈O	Isopropyl alcohol, 95 mm.	...	36	13	v-l 347
		" 190 mm.	...	49.33	12.8	v-l 347
		" 380 mm.	...	63.90	12.6	v-l 347
		" 760 mm.	82.5	80.10	12.0	v-l 347
		" 3087 mm.	...	120.45	11.7	v-l 347
		" 150°-300° C.	...			v-l 14
		"	...	Evaporation data		196
		"	Effect of dissolved salt		v-l	265
116	C₃H₈O₂	2-Methoxyethanol, 100 mm.	...	51.5	80.5	v-l 152
		" 752 mm.	...	99.2	81	v-l 152
		" 150 mm.	79.2	Nonazeotrope		334
		" 760 mm.	124.6	99.9	84.7	334
		" 100 p.s.i.g.	212	169	73.3	334
117	C₃H₈O₂	1,2-Propanediol	188	Nonazeotrope	v-l	60
118	C₃H₈O₂	1,3-Propanediol	214.8	Nonazeotrope	v-l	334
119	C₃H₉N	Propylamine	47.8	Nonazeotrope		334
120	C₃H₉N	Trimethylamine	3.2	75.5	10	v-l 148
		" 0°-100° C.	...			v-l 148
121	C₃H₉NO	1-Amino-2-propanol	159.9	Nonazeotrope		334
122	C₃HF₇O₂	Perfluorobutyric acid	122.0	97	71	222
123	C₄H₅N	3-Butenenitrile	118.9	89.4	34	334
124	C₄H₅N	Methacrylonitrile	...	76.5	16	269
125	C₄H₆ClN	2-Chloro-2-methyl-propionitrile	116	87	22	269
126	C₄H₆O	Crotonaldehyde, 111 mm.	84.9	40	19	334
		" 273 mm.	112.3	60	22	334
		" 412 mm.	126.4	70	23	334
		"	102.4	84	24.8	96, 142, 334
127	C₄H₆O	Methacrylaldehyde	68.0	63.6	7.7	269, 334
128	C₄H₆O₂	3-Butenoic acid	...	Nonazeotrope		334
129	C₄H₆O₂	trans-Crotonic acid	185	Nonazeotrope		334
130	C₄H₆O₂	Crotonic acid	...	99.9	97.8	84
131	C₄H₆O₂	Butyrolactone	204.3	Nonazeotrope		334
132	C₄H₆O₂	Vinyl acetate	72.7	66	7.3	334
133	C₄H₆O₃	Propylene carbonate	242.1	Nonazeotrope		334
134	C₄H₇ClO	2-Chloroethyl vinyl ether	109.1	84	17	334
135	C₄H₇N	Butyronitrile	117.6	88.7	32.5	334
136	C₄H₇NO	2-Hydroxyisobutyro-nitrile, 30 mm.	...	Nonazeotrope		334
		" 50 mm.	...	Nonazeotrope		334

		B-Component		Azeotropic Data		
No.	Formula	Name	B.P.,°C.	B.P.,°C.	Wt.%A	Ref.
A =	H₂O	Water (continued)	100			
137	C₄H₈Cl₂O	Bis(2-chloroethyl) ether	179.2	98	65.5	334
138	C₄H₈O	2-Butanone	79.6	73.4	11.0	78
		" 3.5 p.s.i.g.	...	79.3	12.1	78
		" 9.2 p.s.i.g.	...	88.0	12.5	78
		" 30 p.s.i.g.	...	111	15.8	78
		" 60 p.s.i.g.	...	125	18.3	78
		" 14.7 p.s.i.a.	...	73.3	11.6 v-l	254
		" 50 p.s.i.a.	...	112.2	15.9	254
		" 100 p.s.i.a.	...	139.0	19.3	254
		" 250 p.s.i.a.	...	180.7	23.4	254
		" 500 p.s.i.a.	...	216.1	26.4	254
		"		Evaporation behavior		196
139	C₄H₈O	Butyraldehyde	74.8	68.0	9.7	334
		"	...	67.8	6.7	84
140	C₄H₈O	Ethyl vinyl ether	35.5	34.6	1.5	334
141	C₄H₈O	Isobutyraldehyde	63.5	64.3	6.7	84
142	C₄H₈O	Methyl propenyl ether	46.3	46.3	0.5	334
143	C₄H₈OS	2-Methylthiopropional- dehyde, 85 mm.	...	48	64	76
		" 412 mm.	...	82	60	76
		" 753 mm.	...	97.5	68	76
		" 759 mm.	...	97.5	63	76
144	C₄H₈OS	1,4-Oxathiane	149.2	95.6	48	334
145	C₄H₈O₂	p-Dioxane	Effect of dissolved salt		v-l	265
		" 260 mm.	...	60	15.4	60
146	C₄H₈O₂	Ethoxyacetaldehyde	105	90	21.8	77
147	C₄H₈O₂	2-Hydroxybutyr- aldehyde, 80 mm.	...	Nonazeotrope		334
148	C₄H₈O₂	Isobutyric acid	154.5	98.8	71.8	84
149	C₄H₈O₂	3-Methoxypropional- dehyde, 100 mm.	...	45	30	334
150	C₄H₈O₂	2-Methyl-1,3-dioxolane	82.5	75	8	76
151	C₄H₈O₂	Methyl propionate	79.7	71.0	8.2	84
152	C₄H₈O₂	2-Vinyloxyethanol	143	98	65	94
153	C₄H₉NO	Morpholine	128.3	Nonazeotrope		334
154	C₄H₉NO₂	N-(2-Hydroxyethyl) acetamide	...	Nonazeotrope		334
155	C₄H₁₀O	Butyl alcohol	...	Evaporation behavior		196
		" 250-2500 mm.	...	... ... v-l		251
		" 30 mm.	48	28	52.4	335
156	C₄H₁₀O	sec-Butyl alcohol	99.5	87.0	26.8 v-l	352
		"	...	Evaporation behavior		196
		"	99.5	88.5	32	334
		" 20 mm.	27.3	16.0	32.2	147
157	C₄H₁₀O	Ethyl ether, 20 p.s.i.g.	62	60	2.0	334
158	C₄H₁₀O	Isobutyl alcohol, 745 mm.	...	... ... v-l		335
159	C₄H₁₀O₂	1,2-Dimethoxyethane, 100 mm.	35	...	6	9
		"	85.2	...	10.4	9
		"	85	77.4	10.1	76
160	C₄H₁₀O₂	2-Ethoxyethanol, <100 mm.	...	Nonazeotrope		18
		" 200 mm.	...	66.4	70 v-l	18
		" 400 mm.	...	82.4	79 v-l	18
		"	134	98.2	87 v-l	18
		" 200 mm.	96.5	66.4	85	334
		" 400 mm.	115.6	82.4	76	334
		"	135.6	99.4	71.2	334
161	C₄H₁₀O₃	Diethylene glycol,	...	Nonazeotrope v-l		60
		" 10 mm.	...	Nonazeotrope v-l		60
162	C₄H₁₁N	Butylamine, 575 mm.	69	69	1.3	334
		" 20 p.s.i.g.	106	-	6.5	334

TABLE I   BINARY SYSTEMS   11

			B-Component		Azeotropic Data		
No.	Formula	Name	B.P.,°C.	B.P.,°C.	Wt.%A		Ref.
A =	**H₂O**	**Water (continued)**	**100**				
163	C₄H₁₁N	Diethylamine		Effect of NaOH on		v-l	150
	"		55.5	Nonazeotrope		v-l	149, 334
164	C₄H₁₁NO	2-Dimethylamino-					
		ethanol, 27 p.s.i.g.	174	-	90.2		334
	" 744 mm.		133.9	99	92.6		334
	" 540 mm.		123.4	91	95.2		334
	" 250 mm.		100.7	71	98.2		334
165	C₄H₁₁NO₂	2,2'-Iminodiethanol	...	Nonazeotrope			334
166	C₅H₄O₂	2-Furaldehyde,					
		1-18 atm.	161.7	-	-	v-l	216
167	C₅H₅N	Pyridine	115.3	93.6	41.3		147
	" 120 mm.		...	-	46.2		117
	" 758 mm.		...	-	40.5		117
	" >760 mm.		...	30	40.7	v-l	146
	" >760 mm.		...	50	-	v-l	146
	" >760 mm.		...	80	40.7		146, 360
	"		Effect of dissolved salt			v-l	265
168	C₅H₆N₂	2-Methylpyrazine,					
		737 mm.	133	97	55		351
	"		130	92.6	36 vol. %		279
169	C₅H₆O	2-Methylfuran, 740 mm.	62.7	57.3	3.4	v-l	310
170	C₅H₇N	3-Methyl-3-butene-					
		nitrile	137.0	93.0	43.2		334
171	C₅H₈O	Allyl vinyl ether	67.4	60	5.4		334
172	C₅H₈O	Cyclopentanone	130.8	94.6	42.4	v-l	334
	" 740 mm.		130	92.6	36 vol. %		279
173	C₅H₈O	1-Methoxy-1,3-buta-					
		diene	90.7	76.2	12.7		334
174	C₅H₈O	3-Penten-2-one	123.5	92	28.6		334
175	C₅H₈O	3-Methyl-3-butene-					
		2-one	97.9	81.5	18.4		334
176	C₅H₈O	4-Pentenal	106	84.3	21		334
177	C₅H₈O₂	Allyl acetate	104.1	83	16.7		334
178	C₅H₈O₂	Ethyl acrylate	99.5	81.1	15		283
	" 195 mm.		61	48	12		334
179	C₅H₈O₂	Isopropenyl acetate,					
	" 200 mm.		60.2	48	11		334
	"		97.4	79.3	13.4		334
180	C₅H₈O₂	Methyl methacrylate	100.8	83	14		283
181	C₅H₈O₂	2,4-Pentanedione	140.6	94.4	41		334
182	C₅H₈O₂	Δ-Valerolactone	...	Nonazeotrope			334
183	C₅H₈O₂	Vinyl propionate	95.0	79	13		334
184	C₅H₁₀Cl₂O₂	Bis(2-chloroethoxy)					
		methane	218.1	99.4	86.8		334
185	C₅H₁₀N₂	3-Dimethylamino-					
		propionitrile	174.5	99.6	84		334
186	C₅H₁₀O	cis-1-Butenyl methyl					
		ether	72.0	64	6.1		334
187	C₅H₁₀O	trans-1-Butenyl					
		methyl ether	76.7	67	7.2		334
188	C₅H₁₀O	Isopropenyl ethyl ether	61.9	58	2		334
189	C₅H₁₀O	Isopropyl vinyl ether	55.7	51.8	2.7		334
190	C₅H₁₀O	Propyl vinyl ether	65.1	59	5		334
191	C₅H₁₀O	Tetrahydropyran	88	71	8.5		82
192	C₅H₁₀O	Valeraldehyde	103.3	83	19		334
193	C₅H₁₀O	Valeraldehydes					
		(isomers)	98.6	80	17		334
194	C₅H₁₀O₂	Ethyl propionate,					
		350 mm.	76.0	61	13.3		334
195	C₅H₁₀O₂	3-Methoxybutyral-					
		dehyde, 100 mm.	...	50	37		334
	" 200 mm.		...	64	37		334
	"		131	>92	35		334

		B-Component		Azeotropic Data		
No.	Formula	Name	B.P.,°C.	B.P.,°C.	Wt.%A	Ref.
A =	H_2O	**Water (continued)**	**100**			
196	$C_5H_{10}O_2$	Propyl acetate, 200-700 mm.	...		v-1	307
197	$C_5H_{10}O_2$	Valeric acid	185.5	99.8	89	334
198	$C_5H_{10}O_2$	Valeric acid (isomers)	183.2	99.6	85	334
199	$C_5H_{10}O_2$	1-Vinyloxy-2-propanol	...	~100	75	94
200	$C_5H_{10}O_2$	3-Vinyloxy-1-propanol	...	~100	75	94
201	$C_5H_{10}O_3$	3-Ethoxypropionic acid	219.2	Nonazeotrope		334
202	$C_5H_{10}O_3$	3-Methoxybutyric acid	...	Nonazeotrope		334
203	$C_5H_{10}O_3$	Methoxymethyl propionate	...	95	56	334
204	$C_5H_{11}NO$	4-Methylmorpholine	115.6	94.2	24	334
205	C_5H_{12}	Pentane	36.1	34.6	1.4	334
206	$C_5H_{12}N_2$	1-Methylpiperazine	138.0	Nonazeotrope		334
207	$C_5H_{12}O_2$	1,2-Dimethoxypropane	92	80	11	334
208	$C_5H_{12}O_2$	1-Ethoxy-2-propanol	132.2	97.3	50.1	334
209	$C_5H_{12}O_2$	3-Methoxy-1-butanol	161.1	98.5	80	334
210	$C_5H_{12}O_2$	1,5-Pentanediol	242.5	Nonazeotrope		334
211	$C_5H_{12}O_2$	2-Propoxyethanol	151.5	98.8	70	334
212	$C_5H_{13}N$	N-Methylbutylamine	91.1	82.7	15	334
213	$C_5H_{13}NO$	1-Ethylamino-2-propanol	159.4	Nonazeotrope		334
214	$C_5H_{14}N_2$	N,N-Dimethyl-1,3-propanediamine	134.9	Nonazeotrope		334
215	C_6H_7N	Aniline, 742 mm.	...	98.6	80.8	v-1 143
		"　　6 atm.	...	155	76.6	v-1 143
		"　　11 atm.	...	182	76.2	v-1 143
		"　　16.4 atm.	...	200	77.4	v-1 143
216	C_6H_7N	3-Picoline	144.1	97	60	v-1 365
217	C_6H_7N	4-Picoline	144.3	97.35	62.8	v-1 365
		"	...	97.4	63.5	334
218	$C_6H_8N_2$	2,5-Dimethylpyrazine	154	98.5	65	351
219	C_6H_8O	2,5-Dimethylfuran	93.3	77.0	11.7	334
220	C_6H_8O	2,4-Hexadienal	171	98.0	70	334
221	$C_6H_8O_2$	1,3-Butadienyl acetate	138.5	93	35.6	334
222	$C_6H_8O_2$	Vinyl crotonate	133.9	92	31	334
223	$C_6H_9N_3$	3,3'-Iminodipropionitrile	...	Nonazeotrope		334
224	C_6H_{10}	2-Ethyl-1,3-butadiene	66.9	60.2	5.3	334
225	$C_6H_{10}O$	Cyclohexanone, <760 mm.	...	90	...	v-1 121
		"	155.6	96.3	55	v-1 121
		"	155.4	95	61.6	334
226	$C_6H_{10}O$	2-Ethylcrotonaldehyde	135.3	92.7	38	334
227	$C_6H_{10}O$	2-Hexenal	149	95.1	48.6	334
228	$C_6H_{10}O$	5-Penten-2-one	128.9	92.1	35.3	334
229	$C_6H_{10}O$	2-Methyl-2-pentenal	138.2	93.5	40	334
230	$C_6H_{10}O_2$	Ethyl crotonate	137.8	93.5	38	334
231	$C_6H_{10}O_2$	Vinyl butyrate	116.7	87.2	20.4	334
232	$C_6H_{10}O_2$	Vinyl isobutyrate	105.4	83.5	17	334
233	$C_6H_{10}O_4$	Ethylene glycol diacetate	190.8	99.7	84.6	334
234	$C_6H_{11}N$	Diallylamine	110.5	87.2	24	334
235	$C_6H_{11}NO$	6-Caprolactam, 50-760 mm.	...	...	...	v-1 333
236	$C_6H_{11}NO_3$	2-Methyl-2-nitropropyl vinyl ether, 10 mm.	77-78	...	8.6	341
237	C_6H_{12}	Cyclohexane	80.8	69.5	8.4	147
238	C_6H_{12}	4-Methyl-2-pentene	56.7	53.5	3.5	334
239	$C_6H_{12}Cl_2O$	Bis(chloroisopropyl) ether	187.0	98.5	62.6	334
240	$C_6H_{12}Cl_2O_2$	1,2-Bis(2-chloroethoxy)ethane	240.9	99.7	94.0	334
241	$C_6H_{12}O$	Butyl vinyl ether	94.2	77.5	11.6	334

TABLE I   BINARY SYSTEMS   13

		B-Component		Azeotropic Data		
No.	Formula	Name	B.P.,°C.	B.P.,°C.	Wt.%A	Ref.
A =	H$_2$O	Water (continued)	100			
242	C$_6$H$_{12}$O	Cyclohexanol, 42 mm.	...	35	86	374
		" 57 mm.	...	40	84.8	374
		" 95 mm.	...	50	82.5	374
		" 158 mm.	...	60	80.2	374
		" 252 mm.	...	70	77.8	374
		" 385 mm.	...	80	75.2	374
		" 570 mm.	...	90	72.6	374
		" 684 mm.	...	95	70.7	374
		"	160.65	97.8	69.5	374
		" <760 mm.	160.65	90	74	v-1 122
243	C$_6$H$_{12}$O	2-Ethylbutyraldehyde	116.7	87.5	23.7	334
244	C$_6$H$_{12}$O	Isobutyl vinyl ether	83.4	70.5	7.8	334
245	C$_6$H$_{12}$O	Hexaldehyde	128.3	91.0	31.3	334
246	C$_6$H$_{12}$O	2-Methylpentanal	118.3	88.5	23	334
247	C$_6$H$_{12}$OS	2-Ethylthioethyl vinyl ether	169.7	97.8	61	334
248	C$_6$H$_{12}$O$_2$	2-Ethylbutyric acid	194.2	99.7	87	334
249	C$_6$H$_{12}$O$_2$	Hexanoic acid	205.7	99.8	92.1	334
250	C$_6$H$_{12}$O$_2$	4-Hydroxy-4-methyl-2-pentanone	...	Nonazeotrope		v-1 125
		" 100 mm.	...	Nonazeotrope		v-1 125
		" 200 mm.	123.5	66.4	97	v-1 125
		" 400 mm.	143	82.6	90	v-1 125
		" 760 mm.	161	99.5	85	v-1 125
		"	169.2	99.6	87	335
251	C$_6$H$_{12}$O$_2$	2-Ethyl-2-methyl-1,3-dioxolane	117.6	88.5	20	334
252	C$_6$H$_{12}$O$_2$	2-Methylpentanoic acid	196.4	99.4	87.9	334
253	C$_6$H$_{12}$O$_2$	4-Vinyloxy-1-butanol	-	Min. b.p.		94
254	C$_6$H$_{12}$O$_2$	Tetrahydropyran-2-methanol	187.2	Nonazeotrope		334
255	C$_6$H$_{12}$O$_3$	2-Ethoxyethyl acetate	156.2	97.5	55.6	334
256	C$_6$H$_{12}$O$_3$	Methyl 3-ethoxy-propionate, 50 mm.	...	37	50	334
257	C$_6$H$_{12}$O$_3$	2-(2-Vinyloxyethoxy)ethanol	...	~100	97-8	94
		"	207.6	Nonazeotrope		334
258	C$_6$H$_{13}$Cl	1-Chlorohexane	134.5	91.8	29.7	334
259	C$_6$H$_{13}$N	Cyclohexylamine, 40 mm.	51.4	31.7	69.0	38
		" 70 mm.	...	41.9	66.0	38
		" 100 mm.	72	49.0	64.1	38
		" 200 mm.	90.9	63.6	60.7	38
		" 300 mm.	102.5	72.7	59.1	38
		" 500 mm.	118.9	85.3	57.0	38
		" 760 mm.	134.5	96.4	55.8	38
260	C$_6$H$_{13}$N	Hexamethyleneimine	138	95.5	49.5	81
261	C$_6$H$_{13}$NO	2,6-Dimethyl-morpholine	146.6	99.6	70	334
262	C$_6$H$_{13}$NO	4-Ethylmorpholine	138.3	96.7	46.2	334
263	C$_6$H$_{13}$NO$_2$	4-Morpholineethanol	225.5	Nonazeotrope		334
264	C$_6$H$_{14}$	Hexane	68.7	61.6	5.6	334
265	C$_6$H$_{14}$N$_2$	2,5-Dimethylpipera-zine	164	Nonazeotrope		334
266	C$_6$H$_{14}$N$_2$O	4-(2-Aminoethyl)morpholine	204.7	Nonazeotrope		334
267	C$_6$H$_{14}$N$_2$O	1-Piperazineethanol	246.3	Nonazeotrope		334
268	C$_6$H$_{14}$O	Butyl ethyl ether	92.2	76.6	11.9	334
269	C$_6$H$_{14}$O	2-Ethyl-1-butanol	147.0	96.7	58	335
270	C$_6$H$_{14}$O	Hexyl alcohol	157.1	97.8	67.2	335
271	C$_6$H$_{14}$O	Isopropyl ether, 131 mm.	22.47	20.0	2.6	334
		" 297 mm.	41.82	38.0	3.4	334
		" 481 mm.	54.75	50.0	4.0	334
		" 1520 mm.	92	88	7.6	334

		B-Component		Azeotropic Data		
No.	Formula	Name	B.P.,°C.	B.P.,°C.	Wt.%A	Ref.
A =	H_2O	Water (continued)	100			
272	$C_6H_{14}O$	2-Methyl-1-pentanol	148	97.2	60	334
273	$C_6H_{14}O$	4-Methyl-2-pentanol	131.8	94.3	43.3	334
274	$C_6H_{14}O_2$	1,1-Diethoxyethane	102.1	82.6	14.3	334
275	$C_6H_{14}O_2$	1,1-Dimethoxybutane	114	87.3	20.3	334
276	$C_6H_{14}O_2$	1,3-Dimethoxybutane	120.3	89.6	30	334
277	$C_6H_{14}O_2$	1,1-Dimethoxy-2-methylpropane	104.7	83.9	14.3	334
278	$C_6H_{14}O_2$	2-Methyl-1,5-pentanediol	242.4	Nonazeotrope		334
279	$C_6H_{14}O_2$	3-Methyl-1,5-pentanediol	248.4	Nonazeotrope		334
280	$C_6H_{14}O_3$	Bis(2-methoxyethyl) ether, 100 mm.	103	-	89.5	9
		" 760 mm.	162	-	80.2	9
		" 800 mm.	164	-	80	9
		" 760 mm.	164	99.55	78 v-l	76
281	$C_6H_{14}O_3$	2-(2-Ethoxyethoxy)ethanol	202.8	Nonazeotrope		334
282	$C_6H_{15}N$	Diisopropylamine	84.1	74.1	9	334
283	$C_6H_{15}N$	1,3-Dimethylbutyl-amine	108.5	89.5	28.6	334
284	$C_6H_{15}N$	Dipropylamine	109	86.7	-	41
285	$C_6H_{15}N$	N-Ethylbutylamine	111.2	87.5	43.6	334
286	$C_6H_{15}N$	Hexylamine	132.7	95.5	49	334
287	$C_6H_{15}N$	Triethylamine	89.4	Compound formation v-l		315
288	$C_6H_{15}NO$	2-Butylaminoethanol	199.3	Nonazeotrope		334
289	$C_6H_{15}NO$	2-Diethylaminoethanol	162.1	98.9	74.4	334
290	$C_6H_{15}NO$	1-Isopropylamino-2-propanol	164.5	99.8	86	334
291	$C_6H_{15}N_3$	4-(2-Aminoethyl)piperazine	222.0	Nonazeotrope		334
292	$C_6H_{16}N_2$	$\underline{N},\underline{N}$-Diethylethylene-diamine	144.9	99.8	79.5	334
293	$C_6H_{16}N_2$	$\underline{N},\underline{N},\underline{N}',\underline{N}'$-Tetra-methylethylene-diamine	119-22	95.6	30	287
294	C_7H_8	Toluene	110.7	Evaporation behavior		196
		"	110.6	85	20.2	334
295	$C_7H_8O_2$	Guaiacol	205.0	99.5	87.5	96
296	C_7H_9ClO	2-Chloroallylidene diacetate	212.1	99.7	85	334
297	C_7H_9N	2,6-Lutidine	142	96.02	51.8 v-l	365
298	C_7H_9N	Tetrahydrobenzonitrile	195.1	98.8	78.3	334
299	$C_7H_{10}O$	1,2,3,6-Tetrahydro-benzaldehyde	164.2	96.9	60	334
300	$C_7H_{10}O_4$	Allylidene diacetate	-	98.7	71	334
301	C_7H_{12}	2,4-Dimethyl-1,3-pen-tadiene, 750.6 mm.	93.3	76.8	13	334
302	$C_7H_{12}O$	3-Hepten-2-one	162.9	96	55.7	334
303	$C_7H_{12}O_2$	Butyl acrylate	147	94.5	40	76
		"	...	94.3	38	334
		" 100 mm.	...	47.8	41	334
304	$C_7H_{12}O_2$	2-Ethoxy-3,4-dihydro-1,2-pyran	142.9	93.6	34.9	334
305	$C_7H_{12}O_4$	Pimelic acid, 100 mm.	272	Nonazeotrope		334
306	$C_7H_{14}O$	Butyl isopropenyl ether	114.8	86.3	18.8	334
307	$C_7H_{14}O$	3-Heptanone	147.6	94.6	42.2	334
308	$C_7H_{14}O$	4-Heptanone	143.7	94.3	40.5	334
309	$C_7H_{14}O$	5-Methyl-2-hexanone	144	94.7	44	334
		"	...	93.0	75	84
310	$C_7H_{14}O_2$	Amyl acetate (isomers)	146	94	36.2	334

TABLE I   BINARY SYSTEMS   15

		B-Component		Azeotropic Data		
No.	Formula	Name	B.P.,°C.	B.P.,°C.	Wt.%A	Ref.
A =	H_2O	Water (continued)	100			
311	$C_7H_{14}O_3$	Ethyl 3-ethoxy-propionate	170.1	97	63	334
		" 100 mm.	107.8	50.5	71	334
312	$C_7H_{14}O_3$	3-Methoxybutyl acetate	171.3	96.5	65.4	334
313	$C_7H_{14}O_4$	2-(2-Methoxyethoxy)ethyl acetate	208.9	Nonazeotrope		334
314	C_7H_{16}	Heptane	98.4	79.2	12.9	334
315	$C_7H_{16}O$	5-Methyl-2-hexanol	...	96.5	59.1	84
316	$C_7H_{16}O_2$	1-Butoxy-2-methoxy-ethane	149.9	95.6	42	334
317	$C_7H_{16}O_2$	1-Butoxy-2-propanol	170.1	98.6	72	334
318	$C_7H_{16}O_2$	2-Ethyl-1,5-pentane-diol	253.3	Nonazeotrope		334
319	$C_7H_{16}O_3$	1-(2-Ethoxyethoxy)-2-propanol	198.1	Nonazeotrope		334
320	$C_7H_{16}O_3$	2-Ethoxyethyl 2-methoxyethyl ether	-	99.5	82	334
321	$C_7H_{16}O_3$	2-(2-Propoxyethoxy)ethanol	215.8	Nonazeotrope		334
322	$C_7H_{17}NO$	1-Diethylamino-2-propanol	159.5	97.2	55	334
323	$C_7H_{18}N_2$	3-Diethylamino-propylamine	169.4	99.8	93	334
324	C_8H_8	Styrene	145.1	93.9	40.9	334
325	$C_8H_8Cl_2O_2$	2-(2,4-Dichloro-phenoxy)ethanol	...	~100	~99.6	334
326	C_8H_8O	Acetophenone	201.6	99.1	81.5	334
327	C_8H_8	(Epoxyethyl)benzene	194.2	99.2	77.6	334
328	C_8H_{10}	Ethylbenzene	136.2	92	33.0	334
		"	...	91	30.6	84
329	C_8H_{10}	m-Xylene	139.1	94.5	40	334
330	$C_8H_{10}O$	α-Methylbenzyl alcohol	203.4	99.7	89	335
331	$C_8H_{11}N$	N-Ethylaniline	204.8	99.2	83.9	334
332	$C_8H_{11}N$	α-Methylbenzylamine	188.6	99.4	83.8	334
333	$C_8H_{11}N$	2-Methyl-5-ethyl-pyridine	178.3	98.4	72	334
334	$C_8H_{11}N$	ar-Methyl-1,2,3,6-tetrahydrobenzo-nitrile	205.4	99.1	82.6	334
335	$C_8H_{12}O$	2-Methyl-1,2,3,6-tetrahydrobenz-aldehyde	176.4	97.7	92.2	334
336	$C_8H_{12}O_2$	3,4-Dihydro-2,5-dimethyl-2H-pyran-2-carboxaldehyde	170.9	97.4	56	334
337	$C_8H_{12}O_4$	Diethyl fumarate	218.1	99.5	87.5	334
338	C_8H_{14}	Diisobutylene	102.3	82	12	334
339	$C_8H_{14}O$	Bicyclo[2.2.1]heptane-2-methanol	203.9	99.7	91	334
340	$C_8H_{14}O$	Diisobutylene oxide	...	94	37	334
341	$C_8H_{14}O$	2-Ethyl-2-hexenal	176	97.6	60.9	334
342	$C_8H_{14}O$	2-Octenal	...	99.2	76.2	334
343	$C_8H_{14}O_2$	1,1-Diallyloxyethane	150.9	95.3	41	334
344	$C_8H_{14}O_2$	2-Ethyl-3-hexenoic acid	231.8	99.9	97.4	334
345	$C_8H_{14}O_2$	Vinyl 2-methyl-valerate	148.8	95	38	334
346	$C_8H_{14}O_3$	Bis(2-vinyloxyethyl) ether	198.7	99.4	82	334
347	$C_8H_{14}O_3$	Butyl acetoacetate	213.9	99.4	84.1	334
348	$C_8H_{14}O_4$	Diethyl succinate	216.2	99.9	91	334
349	$C_8H_{15}N$	2-(Aminomethyl)bicyclo[2.2.1]heptane	185.9	99	82	334
350	$C_8H_{16}O$	2-Ethylhexaldehyde	163.6	96.4	51.6	334

		B-Component		Azeotropic Data		
No.	Formula	Name	B.P.,°C.	B.P.,°C.	Wt.%A	Ref.
A =	H_2O	Water (continued)	100			
351	$C_8H_{16}O$	2,4,4-Trimethyl-1,2-epoxypentane	140.9	93.4	33	334
352	$C_8H_{16}O$	2,4,4-Trimethyl-2,3-epoxypentane	127.3	91	25	334
353	$C_8H_{16}OS$	2-Butylthioethyl vinyl ether	210.5	99.3	80	334
354	$C_8H_{16}O_2$	2-Butoxyethyl vinyl ether	...	97.0	52.8	334
355	$C_8H_{16}O_2$	2,3-Epoxy-2-ethyl-hexanol	...	100	99.5	334
356	$C_8H_{16}O_2$	2-Ethylbutyl acetate	162.3	97.0	52.4	334
357	$C_8H_{16}O_2$	2-Ethylhexanoic acid	227.6	99.9	96.4	334
	''		...	99.5	97.6	84
358	$C_8H_{16}O_2$	Hexyl acetate	171.0	97.4	61	334
359	$C_8H_{16}O_2$	Iso-octanoic acid (isomers)	220	99.9	96	334
360	$C_8H_{16}O_2$	4-Methyl-2-pentyl acetate	146.1	94.8	36.7	334
361	$C_8H_{16}O_3$	2-Butoxyethyl acetate	192.2	98.8	71.9	334
362	$C_8H_{16}O_3$	2,5-Diethoxytetra-hydrofuran	173.0	98	60	334
363	$C_8H_{16}O_3$	2-Ethoxyethyl 2-vinyloxyethyl ether	194.0	99.3	82.3	334
364	$C_8H_{16}O_4$	2-(2-Ethoxyethoxy) ethyl acetate	217.4	Nonazeotrope		334
365	$C_8H_{17}Cl$	1-Chloro-2-ethyl-hexane	173	97.3	55	334
366	$C_8H_{17}N$	N-Ethylcyclohexyl-amine	164.9	97.1	58	334
367	$C_8H_{17}N$	5-Ethyl-2-methyl-piperidine	163.4	97.1	57.0	334
368	$C_8H_{17}N$	ar-Methylcyclo-hexylmethylamine	...	99.0	79	334
369	$C_8H_{17}NO$	4-Ethyl-2,6-dimethyl-morpholine	158.1	97.5	49	334
370	C_8H_{18}	Octane	125.7	89.6	25.5	334
371	$C_8H_{18}O$	2-Ethyl-1-hexanol	184.8	99.1	80	335
372	$C_8H_{18}O$	Iso-octyl alcohol (isomers)	186.5	99.8	82	334
373	$C_8H_{18}O_2$	2-Ethyl-1,3-hexanediol	243.1	Nonazeotrope		334
374	$C_8H_{18}O_2$	1-Butoxy-2-ethoxy-ethane	164.2	96.8	50	334
375	$C_8H_{18}O_2$	1,1-Diethoxybutane	146.3	94.2	34.5	334
376	$C_8H_{18}O_2$	5-Ethoxy-3-methyl-pentanol	211.7	99.9	97	334
377	$C_8H_{18}O_2$	2-Ethyl-3-methyl-1,5-pentanediol	265.5	Nonazeotrope		334
378	$C_8H_{18}O_2$	2-Hexyloxyethanol	208.1	99.7	91	334
379	$C_8H_{18}O_2$	2-(2-Methylpentyloxy) ethanol	197.1	99.6	86	334
380	$C_8H_{18}O_3$	2-(2-Butoxyethoxy) ethanol	230.6	Nonazeotrope		334
381	$C_8H_{18}O_3$	Bis(2-ethoxyethyl) ether	188.4	99.4	69	334
382	$C_8H_{18}O_4$	1,2-Bis(2-methoxy-ethoxy)ethane	...	Nonazeotrope		9
383	$C_8H_{19}N$	Dibutylamine	159.6	97	50.5	334
384	$C_8H_{19}N$	2-Ethylhexylamine	169.1	98.2	64	334
385	$C_8H_{19}NO$	2-Diisopropylamino-ethanol	190.9	99.2	85	334
386	$C_8H_{19}NO_2$	2,2'-Butyliminodi-ethanol	...	Nonazeotrope		334
387	$C_8H_{19}NO_2$	1,1'-Ethyliminodi-2-propanol	238.9	Nonazeotrope		334
388	$C_9H_8O_2$	Vinyl benzoate	...	99.3	82.6	334

TABLE I BINARY SYSTEMS   **17**

		B-Component		Azeotropic Data		
No.	Formula	Name	B.P.,°C.	B.P.,°C.	Wt.%A	Ref.
A =	H_2O	Water (continued)	100			
389	$C_9H_{10}O_2$	1,2-Epoxy-3-phenoxypropane	244.4	99.8	96.1	334
390	$C_9H_{11}N$	5-Ethyl-2-vinyl-pyridine	...	99.4	85	334
391	C_9H_{12}	Cumene	152.4	95	43.8	334
392	$C_9H_{12}O_2$	Bicyclo[2.2.1]hept-5-ene-2-ol acetate	188.6	98.6	70	334
393	$C_9H_{13}NO$	5-Ethyl-2-pyridine-ethanol	...	Nonazeotrope		334
394	$C_9H_{14}O$	Isophorone	215.2	99.5	83.9	334
		" 25 p.s.i.g.	251	130	86.5	334
395	$C_9H_{15}O$	1-Methyl-2,5-endomethylene-cyclohexane-1-methanol	211.1	99.7	90.6	334
396	$C_9H_{15}N$	Triallylamine	151.1	95	38	334
397	$C_9H_{16}O$	5-Ethyl-3-hepten-2-one	193.5	98.7	73.4	334
398	$C_9H_{16}O_4$	Dimethyl pimelate	248.9	99.9	96.8	334
399	$C_9H_{18}O$	2,6-Dimethyl-4-heptanone	169.4	97.0	51.9	334
400	$C_9H_{18}O_2$	2-Heptyl acetate	176.4	97.8	58.9	334
401	$C_9H_{18}O_2$	3-Heptyl acetate	173.8	97.5	57.6	334
402	$C_9H_{18}O_3$	3-(2-Ethylbutoxy)propionic acid	...	100	> 99	334
403	C_9H_{20}	Nonane	150.7	94.8	82	332
		"	150.8	95	39.8	334
404	$C_9H_{20}O$	2,6-Dimethyl-4-heptanol	178.1	98.5	70.4	335
405	$C_9H_{20}O_2$	2-Ethyl-2-butyl-1,3-propanediol	...	Nonazeotrope		334
406	$C_9H_{20}O_3$	1-(2-Butoxyethoxy)-2-propanol	230.3	99.9	95	334
407	$C_9H_{20}O_3$	2-Methoxymethyl-2,4-dimethyl-1,5-pentanediol	...	Nonazeotrope		334
408	$C_9H_{20}O_3$	1,1,3-Triethoxy-propane	...	99	70	334
409	$C_9H_{21}N$	N-Methyldibutylamine	163.1	96.5	48.0	334
410	$C_9H_{21}N$	Tripropylamine	156	94.3	-	41
411	$C_9H_{21}NO_2$	1,1'-Isopropylimino-di-2-propanol	248.6	Nonazeotrope		334
412	$C_9H_{21}NO_4$	2-(2-[2-(3-Amino-propoxy)ethoxy]-ethoxy)ethanol	...	Nonazeotrope		334
413	$C_{10}H_{10}O_4$	Dimethyl phthalate	282.9	100	98.9	334
414	$C_{10}H_{12}O_3$	2-Phenoxyethyl acetate	260.6	99.9	97.4	334
415	$C_{10}H_{14}$	Dicyclopentadiene	172	98	67.7	334
416	$C_{10}H_{14}N_2$	Nicotine, 110 mm.	...	Nonazeotrope	v-l	106
		" 478 mm.	...	...	99.70 v-l	106
		" 572 mm.	...	...	99.02 v-l	106
		" 624 mm.	...	...	98.50 v-l	106
		" 760 mm.	...	99.85	97.48 v-l	106
417	$C_{10}H_{14}O_2$	Ethyl bicyclo[2.2.1]hept-5-ene-2-carboxylate	198	99.2	80	334
418	$C_{10}H_{14}O_3$	2-(2-Phenoxyethoxy)ethanol	297.9	Nonazeotrope		334
419	$C_{10}H_{15}N$	N-Butylaniline	240.4	99.8	94.4	334
420	$C_{10}H_{15}N$	N-Ethyl-α-methyl-benzylamine	201.2	99.2	80	334
421	$C_{10}H_{15}N$	N,N,α-Trimethyl-benzylamine	195.8	98.6	74.8	334

		B-Component		Azeotropic Data		
No.	Formula	Name	B.P.,°C.	B.P.,°C.	Wt.%A	Ref.
A =	H_2O	Water (continued)	100			
422	$C_{10}H_{15}NO$	2-(α-Methylbenzyl-amino)ethanol	...	Nonazeotrope		334
423	$C_{10}H_{16}O$	Dicyclopentenol	...	100	96.6	334
424	$C_{10}H_{16}O$	Trimethyltetrahydro-benzaldehyde	204.5	99.0	77.0	334
425	$C_{10}H_{16}O_4$	Diisopropyl maleate	228.7	99.9	93	334
426	$C_{10}H_{18}O_2$	Vinyl 2-ethylhexanoate	185.2	98.6	68	334
427	$C_{10}H_{18}O_2$	Vinyl octanoate (isomers)	...	99.1	74	334
428	$C_{10}H_{20}O$	2-Ethylhexyl vinyl ether	177.7	97.8	59.1	334
429	$C_{10}H_{20}O_2$	2-Ethylbutyl butyrate	199.6	98.6	74.9	334
430	$C_{10}H_{20}O_2$	2-Ethylhexyl acetate	198.4	99.0	73.5	334
431	$C_{10}H_{20}O_2$	4-Methyl-2-pentyl butyrate	182.6	98.2	60.8	334
432	$C_{10}H_{20}O_3$	2-Butoxyethyl 2-vinyloxyethyl ether	226.7	99.8	90	334
433	$C_{10}H_{21}Cl$	Chlorodecane (isomers)	210.6	99.7	84	334
434	$C_{10}H_{21}N$	N-Butylcyclohexyl-amine	209.5	99.5	81	334
435	$C_{10}H_{22}O$	Decyl alcohol (isomers)	217.3	100	94.8	335
436	$C_{10}H_{22}O$	2-Ethyloctanol	220.5	99.9	94.0	334
437	$C_{10}H_{22}O$	2-Propylheptanol	217.9	99.8	92	334
438	$C_{10}H_{22}O_2$	1,2-Dibutoxyethane	203.6	99.1	76.8	334
439	$C_{10}H_{22}O_2$	1,1-Diisobutoxyethane	160.5	97.4	52.5	334
440	$C_{10}H_{22}O_3$	2-(2-Hexyloxyethoxy)ethanol	259.1	100	98.1	334
441	$C_{10}H_{22}O_4$	1,2-Bis(2-ethoxy-ethoxy)ethane	246.9	Nonazeotrope		334
442	$C_{10}H_{22}O_5$	Bis[2-(2-methoxy-ethoxy)ethyl] ether	...	Nonazeotrope		9, 334
443	$C_{10}H_{23}N$	Decylamine (isomers)	203.7	99.5	82	334
444	$C_{10}H_{23}N$	Diamylamine (isomers)	190	99.3	76	334
445	$C_{10}H_{23}N$	N,N-Dimethyl-2-ethyl-hexylamine	176.1	98.2	58	334
446	$C_{10}H_{23}NO$	2-Dibutylaminoethanol	228.7	99.9	91.0	334
447	$C_{11}H_{14}O_3$	Butyl salicylate	268.2	99.9	95.8	334
448	$C_{11}H_{14}O_3$	Ethyl 6-formylbicyclo[2.2.1]hept-5-en-2-carboxylate	...	100	97	334
449	$C_{11}H_{16}O_3$	Allyl 6-methyl-3,4-epoxycyclohexane-carboxylate	251.4	100	98.1	334
450	$C_{11}H_{18}O_2$	Isopropyl 6-methyl-3-cyclohexene-carboxylate	215.2	99.7	84	334
451	$C_{11}H_{20}O$	5-Ethyl-3-nonen-2-one	226.4	99.6	92	334
452	$C_{11}H_{20}O_4$	Diethyl pimelate	268.1	100	98.3	334
453	$C_{11}H_{22}O$	5-Ethyl-2-nonanone	222.9	99.6	87.1	334
454	$C_{11}H_{22}O_2$	2,6-Dimethyl-4-heptyl acetate	192.2	98.7	67.6	334
455	$C_{11}H_{22}O_3$	4-Methoxy-2,6-dipropyl-1,3-dioxane	223.6	99.6	88.1	334
456	$C_{11}H_{24}$	Undecane	194.5	98.85	96	332
457	$C_{11}H_{24}O$	5-Ethyl-2-nonanol	225.4	99.7	89.1	334
458	$C_{11}H_{24}O_2$	2,2-Dibutoxypropane	...	98.9	69.6	334
459	$C_{11}H_{24}O_2$	2,6-Dimethyl-4-heptyloxyethanol	225.5	99.9	91	334
460	$C_{11}H_{24}O_4$	1,1,3,3-Tetraethoxy-propane	220.1	99.8	87.4	334

TABLE I   BINARY SYSTEMS   **19**

		B-Component		Azeotropic Data		
No.	Formula	Name	B.P.,°C.	B.P.,°C.	Wt.%A	Ref.

A = H_2O Water (continued) **100**

No.	Formula	Name	B.P.,°C.	B.P.,°C.	Wt.%A	Ref.
461	$C_{11}H_{25}NO$	1-Dibutylamino-2-propanol	229.1	99.8	88.4	334
462	$C_{12}H_{14}O_4$	Diethyl phthalate	294.3	99.9	98.4	334
463	$C_{12}H_{18}O$	Triisobutylene oxide	...	99.3	72	334
464	$C_{12}H_{19}N$	N-Butyl-α-methyl-benzylamine	239.3	99.8	92	334
465	$C_{12}H_{20}O_2$	sec-Butyl-6-methyl-3-cyclohexene-carboxylate	...	100	92	334
466	$C_{12}H_{20}O_4$	Dibutyl fumarate	285.2	99.9	98.5	334
467	$C_{12}H_{20}O_4$	Dibutyl maleate	280.6	99.9	98.4	334
468	$C_{12}H_{22}O_2$	2-Ethylhexyl crotonate	241.2	99.9	93.4	334
469	$C_{12}H_{22}O_2$	Vinyl decanoate (isomers)	...	99.9	88	334
470	$C_{12}H_{22}O_4$	Diethyl 2-ethyl-3-methylglutarate	255.8	100	97.1	334
471	$C_{12}H_{23}N$	Dicyclohexylamine	255.8	Nonazeotrope		38
472	$C_{12}H_{24}O$	2,6,8-Trimethyl-4-nonanone	218.2	99	84	334
473	$C_{12}H_{24}O_2$	2-Ethylbutyl 2-ethylbutyrate	222.6	99.6	85.6	334
474	$C_{12}H_{24}O_2$	2-Ethylbutyl hexanoate	236.2	99.7	91.2	334
475	$C_{12}H_{24}O_2$	Hexyl 2-ethylbutyrate	230.3	99.7	88.8	334
476	$C_{12}H_{24}O_2$	Hexyl hexanoate	245.2	99.8	93.3	334
477	$C_{12}H_{26}$	Dodecane	214.5	99.45	98	332
478	$C_{12}H_{26}O$	2-Butyl-1-octanol	253.4	99.9	97.5	334
479	$C_{12}H_{26}O$	2,6,8-Trimethyl-4-nonanol	225.5	99.6	89.7	335
480	$C_{12}H_{26}O_2$	1,1-Diethoxy-2-ethylhexane	207.8	99.3	78.6	334
481	$C_{12}H_{26}O_2$	1,1-Diisopentoxyethane	213.6	99.3	78.8	334
482	$C_{12}H_{26}O_2$	3-Ethoxy-4-ethyl-octanol	249.2	100	98	334
483	$C_{12}H_{26}O_3$	Bis(2-butoxyethyl) ether	254.6	99.8	94.7	334
484	$C_{12}H_{26}O_3$	1,1,3-Triethoxyhexane	...	99.6	85	334
485	$C_{12}H_{27}N$	Dihexylamine	239.8	99.8	92.8	334
486	$C_{12}H_{27}N$	Tributylamine	213.9	99.8	82	334
487	$C_{12}H_{27}O_4P$	Tributyl phosphate	...	100	99.4	334
488	$C_{13}H_{24}O_2$	Decyl acrylate (isomers)	...	99.9	94.9	334
489	$C_{14}H_{22}O$	2-(Ethylhexyl)phenol	297.0	100	> 99	334
490	$C_{14}H_{23}N$	N-(Ethylhexyl)aniline	...	100	99.3	334
491	$C_{14}H_{24}$	1,3,6,8-Tetramethyl-1,6-cyclodecadiene	220.5	99.5	82.3	334
492	$C_{14}H_{26}O_4$	Dibutyl adipate	...	100	>99	334
493	$C_{14}H_{28}O$	Trimethylnonyl vinyl ether	223.4	99.6	84.3	334
494	$C_{14}H_{28}O_2$	2-Ethylbutyl 2-ethyl-hexanoate	261.5	99.9	95.8	334
495	$C_{14}H_{28}O_2$	2-Ethylhexyl 2-ethyl-butyrate	252.8	99.9	94.8	334
496	$C_{14}H_{28}O_2$	2-Ethylhexyl hexanoate	267.2	99.9	96.4	334
497	$C_{14}H_{28}O_2$	Hexyl 2-ethyl-hexanoate	254.3	99.9	94.6	334
498	$C_{14}H_{29}N$	N-(2-Ethylhexyl)cyclohexylamine	...	100	99.7	334
499	$C_{14}H_{30}O$	7-Ethyl-2-methyl-4-undecanol	264.3	99.9	96.3	334
500	$C_{14}H_{30}O_2$	2-(2,6,8-Trimethyl-4-nonyloxy)ethanol	...	100	99.0	334
501	$C_{15}H_{28}O_4$	Dibutyl pimelate	...	100	> 99.5	334
502	$C_{15}H_{32}O$	2,8-Dimethyl-6-isobutyl-4-nonanol	265.4	99.9	97.2	334

		B-Component			Azeotropic Data		
No.	Formula	Name	B.P.,°C.	B.P.,°C.	Wt.%A		Ref.
A =	H_2O	Water (continued)	100				
503	$C_{16}H_{18}O$	Bis(α-methylbenzyl) ether	286.7	100	98.7		334
504	$C_{16}H_{28}O_4$	Bis(4-methyl-2-pentyl) maleate	...	100	99		334
505	$C_{16}H_{30}O_2$	Tridecyl acrylate	...	100	98.8		334
506	$C_{16}H_{31}N$	Bis(methylcyclohexyl-methyl)amine	...	100	99.45		334
507	$C_{16}H_{32}O_2$	2-Ethylhexyl 2-ethylhexanoate	280.4	99.9	97.9		334
508	$C_{16}H_{34}O$	Bis(2-ethylhexyl) ether	269.8	99.8	96.4		334
509	$C_{16}H_{35}N$	Bis(2-ethylhexyl) amine	280.7	100	97.6		334
510	$C_{17}H_{36}O$	3,9-Diethyl-6-tridecanol	309	100	>99		334
511	$C_{18}H_{24}N_2$	Bis(α-methylbenzyl) ethylenediamine	...	100	>99.9		334
512	$C_{18}H_{38}O_2$	1,1-Bis(2-ethylhexyloxy) ethane	...	99.0	.99.9		334
513	$C_{18}H_{39}NO$	2-[Bis(2-ethylhexyl) amino]ethanol	...	100	>99.5		334
514	$C_{20}H_{36}O_4$	Bis(2-ethylhexyl) fumarate	...	100	>99.9		334
515	$C_{20}H_{36}O_4$	Bis(2-ethylhexyl) maleate	...	100	>99.9		334
516	$C_{20}H_{40}O_3$	2-Ethylhexyl 3-(2-ethylhexyloxy) butyrate	...	100	>99.5		334
517	$C_{20}H_{42}O$	Decyl ether (isomers)	...	100	99.6		334
518	$C_{20}H_{42}O$	Eicosanol (isomers)	...	100	99.8		334
519	$C_{20}H_{43}N$	Didecylamine (isomers)	...	100	99.6		334
520	$C_{21}H_{38}O_3$	Allyl 9,10-epoxystearate	...	Nonazeotrope			334
521	$C_{24}H_{52}O_4Si$	Tetra(2-ethylbutoxy) silane	...	100	99.9		334
522	$C_{31}H_{58}O_6$	Tri(2-ethylhexyl) 1,2,4-butane-tricarboxylate	...	100	99.8		334
A =	H_2S	Hydrogen Sulfide	-59.6				
523	C_2H_6	Ethane, 200 p.s.i.g.	...	-21.6	7.9	v-1	159
		" 300 p.s.i.g.	...	-6.5	11.6	v-1	159
		" 400 p.s.i.g.	...	5	14.5	v-1	159
		" 500 p.s.i.g.	...	15	17.1	v-1	159
		" 600 p.s.i.g.	...	23.5	19.6	v-1	159
524	C_3H_8	Propane, 200 p.s.i.g.	...	7.8	75.2	v-1	161
		" 400 p.s.i.g.	...	37.1	82	v-1	161
		" 600 p.s.i.g.	...	56	83.7	v-1	161
		" 800 p.s.i.g.	...	72	87.2	v-1	161
		" 1000 p.s.i.g.	...	84.2	89.9	v-1	161
		" 1200 p.s.i.g.	...	95	92.7	v-1	161
A =	H_3N	Ammonia	-33.4				
525	C_2H_7N	Ethylamine, 0°-30° C.	...	Nonazeotrope			334
526	C_3H_4	Propadiene	-32	-45	44.3		127
527	C_3H_5F	2-Fluoropropene	-24	-40.5	34		127
528	C_4H_{10}	Butane, 300 p.s.i.g.	...	43	56.8	v-1	160
		" 500 p.s.i.g.	...	66	59.0	v-1	160
		" 700 p.s.i.g.	...	81	60.9	v-1	160
		" 900 p.s.i.g.	...	94	62.1	v-1	160
		" 1100 p.s.i.g.	...	104	63.4	v-1	160
529	C_8H_{18}	Iso-octane, 200-1600 p.s.i.g.	...	...	...	v-1	162
		" >1400 p.s.i.g.		Min. b.p. 98-100%		v-1	162

TABLE I   BINARY SYSTEMS   21

		B-Component			Azeotropic Data		
No.	Formula	Name	B.P.,°C.	B.P.,°C.	Wt.%A		Ref.
A =	He	Helium	-268.9				
530	CH₄	Methane, 5-170 atm.	...	Nonazeotrope		v-1	165
A =	O₂S	Sulfur Dioxide	-10				
531	C₂H₆O	Methyl ether	-23.6	0	65		102
A =	S	Sulfur	444.6				
532	Se	Selenium	688	Compound formation		v-1	6
A =	CCl₂F₂	Dichlorodifluoromethane	-29.8				
533	CHClF₂	Chlorodifluoro-methane	-40.8	-41.4	25		86
		" 4.93 atm.	0.04	0.00	2.1		261
		" 2059 mm.	...	Nonazeotrope			346
534	CH₃Cl	Chloromethane, 5380 mm.	33.5	25.0	78		282
535	C₂H₄F₂	1,1-Difluoroethane	...	-30.5	77.55		260
		"	...	0.00	73.80		260
		"	...	24.90	71.22		260
		"	...	40.08	69.31		260
		" 60 p.s.i.a.	...	4.44	76.2		281
		" 112 p.s.i.a.	...	25	74		281
536	C₂H₆O	Methyl ether, 2340 mm.	6	0	90		282
537	C₃F₆	Hexafluoropropene, 2059 mm.	-6.1	-7.1	46.3	v-1	346
538	C₃HF₇	Heptafluoropropane, 2328 mm.	17	0.00	86.5		261
539	C₄F₈	Perfluorocyclobutane, 2059 mm.	21	Nonazeotrope			346
A =	CCl₃F	Trichlorofluoro-methane	24.9				
540	C₂H₄O	Acetaldehyde	20.2	15.6	55		102
541	C₂H₄O₂	Methyl formate	32	20	82		102
A =	CCl₄	Carbon Tetrachloride	76.74				
542	CH₄O	Methanol	64.7			v-1	245
543	C₂HCl₃	Trichloroethylene	86.2	Ideal system		v-1	184
544	C₂H₃N	Acetonitrile, 371.2 mm.	...	45	84.5	v-1	22
545	C₂H₄Cl₂	1,2-Dichloroethane	83.45	75.5	80		197
546	C₂H₄O₂	Acetic acid, < 50 mm.	...	Nonazeotrope			132
		" 90 mm.	...	18.7	99.28		132
		" 340 mm.	...	51.5	99.42		132
		" 530 mm.	...	64.6	99		132
		" 760 mm.	118.1	76	98.46		132
		" 1080 mm.	...	90	97.7		132
		" 1400 mm.	...	...	97.0		132
547	C₂H₆O	Ethyl alcohol	78.3	65	84	v-1	136
548	C₃H₆O	Acetone, 513.2 mm.	...	45	9	v-1	23
		" 300 mm.	31.29	31.22	9.03	v-1	10
		" 450 mm.	41.56	41.47	11.80	v-1	10
		" 600 mm.	49.36	49.26	12.48	v-1	10
		" 760 mm.	56.08	55.98	12.6	v-1	10
549	C₃H₆O	Allyl alcohol	97.1	72.3	88.5		334
550	C₃H₈O	Propyl alcohol	97.2	72.8	88.5		334
551	C₄H₈O	2-Butanone, 342 mm.	...	50.0	84.3	v-1	108
		"	79.6	73.7	81.6	v-1	108, 184
552	C₄H₈O₂	Ethyl acetate	76.7	74.8	57		334
553	C₄H₁₀O	n-Butyl alcohol	117.75	76.55	97.6	v-1	136
554	C₅H₄O₂	2-Furaldehyde	162	Nonazeotrope		v-1	349
555	C₆H₆	Benzene	80.1	Min. b.p.	98	v-1	245
		" 40° C.	...	Nonazeotrope		v-1	107
		" 760 mm.	80.1	Nonazeotrope		v-1	107
		" >1800 mm.	...	Min. b.p.	...		107
556	C₇H₈	Toluene	110.7	Nonazeotrope		v-1	245, 309

		B-Component		Azeotropic Data		
No.	Formula	Name	B.P.,°C.	B.P.,°C.	Wt.%A	Ref.
A =	CS$_2$	Carbon Disulfide	46.2			
557	CH$_3$I	Iodomethane	42.55	41.2	18.6 v-1	116
558	C$_2$H$_4$Cl$_2$	1,1-Dichloroethane	57.2	46	94	334
559	C$_3$H$_7$Cl	1-Chloropropane	46.6	45.2	55	334
560	C$_4$H$_8$O$_2$	Ethyl acetate	76.7	46.1	97	334
561	C$_4$H$_{10}$O	Ethyl ether	34.6	34.4	1	334
A =	CHClF$_2$	Chlorodifluoro-methane	-40.8 (-17.1°/2059 mm.)			
562	C$_2$ClF$_5$	Chloropentafluoro-ethane	-38.5	-45.6	48.7	15
563	C$_2$H$_2$Cl$_2$F$_2$	1,2-Dichloro-1,2-difluoroethane, 755 mm.	29.8	-41.4	87.6	96
564	C$_3$F$_6$	Hexafluoropropene, 2059 mm.	-6.1	-17.3	69.7	346
565	C$_3$F$_8$	Perfluoropropane, 6.064 atm.	12.5	0	46	261
566	C$_3$H$_8$	Propane, 86.2 p.s.i.a.	...	0	68	280
		" 6.002 atm.	8.6	0	68.3	261
567	C$_4$F$_8$	Perfluorocyclobutane, 2059 mm.	21.0	Nonazeotrope		346
A =	CHCl$_2$F	Dichlorofluoro-methane	7.63/723 mm.			
568	C$_2$Cl$_2$F$_4$	1,2-Dichloro-1,1,2,2-tetrafluoroethane, 723 mm.	2.22	0.00	25	261
A =	CHCl$_3$	Chloroform	61.2			
569	CH$_2$O$_2$	Formic acid	100.75	...	... v-1	56
570	CH$_4$O	Methanol	64.7	...	... v-1	31
		" 400 mm.	...	36.3	88.9 v-1	233
		" 500 mm.	...	41.6	88.4 v-1	233
		" 600 mm.	...	46.2	87.9 v-1	233
571	C$_2$Cl$_4$	Tetrachloroethylene	121.1	Nonazeotrope	v-1	64
572	C$_2$H$_3$N	Acetonitrile	81.6	Nonazeotrope		334
573	C$_2$H$_4$O$_2$	Acetic acid	118.1	Nonazeotrope	v-1	56
574	C$_2$H$_6$O	Ethyl alcohol, 20 p.s.i.g.	101.7	82	89	335
575	C$_3$H$_6$O	Acetone, 101 mm.	...	15	74.3	286
		" 129 mm.	...	20	75.0	286
		" 202 mm.	...	30	76.1	286
		" 250 mm.	...	35	76.3	286
		" 308 mm.	...	40	76.7	286
		" 455 mm.	...	50	77.1	286
		" 546 mm.	...	55	77.3	286
576	C$_3$H$_6$O$_2$	Methyl acetate	57.1	64.74	64.35 v-1	31, 195
577	C$_3$H$_6$O$_2$	Ethyl formate	54.1	62.7	87	195, 252
578	C$_3$H$_7$Br	2-Bromopropane	59.35	62.2	65	195, 252
579	C$_4$H$_8$O	2-Butanone	79.6	Nonazeotrope	v-1	183, 184
	C$_4$H$_8$O	2-Butanone	79.6	79.9	17	334
580	C$_4$H$_8$O$_2$	Isopropyl formate	68.8	70	13	195
581	C$_4$H$_{10}$O	Ethyl ether	34.5	Nonazeotrope	v-1	177
582	C$_6$H$_{12}$O	4-Methyl-2-pentanone	115.9	Nonazeotrope	v-1	157
583	C$_6$H$_{12}$O$_2$	Butyl acetate	126.2	Nonazeotrope	v-1	63
584	C$_9$H$_{10}$O$_2$	Ethyl benzoate	213.3	Nonazeotrope		334
A =	CH$_2$ClBr	Bromochloromethane	69			
585	CH$_2$Cl$_2$	Dichloromethane	40.7	Nonazeotrope		96
A =	CH$_2$Cl$_2$	Dichloromethane	40.0			
586	C$_6$H$_{14}$	2,2-Dimethylbutane, 742 mm.	49.74	35.6	53 vol. %	235

TABLE I   BINARY SYSTEMS   23

		B-Component		Azeotropic Data		
No.	Formula	Name	B.P.,°C.	B.P.,°C.	Wt.%A	Ref.
A =	CH_2O_2	**Formic Acid**	**100.75**			
587	$C_2H_4O_2$	Acetic acid	178.1	Nonazeotrope	v-l	56
588	C_3H_7NO	N,N-Dimethylform-				
		amide	153.0	153.2	1.2	295
		"	...	158.8	...	210
		" 100 mm.	90	98.5	...	v-l	210
		" 200 mm.	107.9	117.0	...	v-l	210
		" 760 mm.	153	158.8	...	v-l	210
589	C_5H_5N	Pyridine	115.5	107.43	61.4	v-l	360
A =	CH_3Cl_3Si	**Trichloromethylsilane**	...			
590	C_3H_9SiCl	Chlorotrimethylsilane	...	V.p. curves, non-azeotrope		179
A =	CH_3NO_2	**Nitromethane**	**101.2**			
591	CH_4O	Methanol	64.51	64.33	12.2	55
592	C_2H_3N	Acetonitrile, 60° C.	...	Nonazeotrope	v-l	22
593	C_2H_6O	Ethyl alcohol	78.32	76.05	29.0	55
594	C_3H_6O	Acetone, 45° C.	...	Nonazeotrope	v-l	22
595	C_3H_8O	Isopropyl alcohol	82.40	79.33	27.6	55
596	C_3H_8O	Propyl alcohol	97.25	Nonazeotrope	v-l	135
		"	97.15	89.09	48.4	55
597	$C_4H_{10}O$	Butyl alcohol	117.73	97.99	71.4	55
598	$C_4H_{10}O$	sec-Butyl alcohol	99.53	91.14	45.8	55
599	$C_4H_{10}O$	tert-Butyl alcohol	82.41	80.04	21.2	55
600	$C_4H_{10}O$	Isobutyl alcohol	107.89	94.46	57.6	55
601	C_6H_6	Benzene	80.1	...	12.7	v-l	343
602	C_6H_{12}	Cyclohexane	80.75	69.5	26.5	v-l	343
A =	CH_4	**Methane**	...			
603	C_2H_6	Ethane	...	Nonazeotrope	v-l	268
604	C_3H_8	Propane	...	Nonazeotrope	v-l	268
A =	CH_4Cl_2Si	**Dichloromethylsilane**	...			
605	C_3H_9ClSi	Chlorotrimethyl-				
		silane, 30°-40°	...	V.p. curve, non-azeotrope		302
A =	CH_4O	**Methanol**	**64.7**			
606	$C_2Cl_3F_3$	1,1,2-Trichlorotri-				
		fluoroethane	47.5	39.9	6	335
607	$C_2H_2Cl_2$	cis-1,2-Dichloro-				
		ethylene	60.3	51.5	15.1	v-l	5
608	$C_2H_2Cl_2$	trans-1,2-Dichloro-				
		ethylene	48.3	41.9	9.02	v-l	5
609	$C_2H_4Cl_2$	1,2-Dichloroethane	83.5	59.5	35	335
610	C_2H_4O	Acetaldehyde	20.2	Nonazeotrope	v-l	171
611	$C_2H_4O_2$	Acetic acid	118.1	Nonazeotrope	v-l	205, 285
612	C_2H_6O	Ethyl alcohol	78.3	Nonazeotrope	v-l	7, 68
613	C_2H_6O	Methyl ether	-23.65	...	...	v-l	130
614	C_3H_3N	Acrylonitrile, 175 mm.	37	29	47	335
615	C_3H_6O	Acetone, 752 mm.	...	55.07	14.8	v-l	7, 130
		"	56.1	Nonazeotrope		192
		" 4.56 atm.	108	102	32	335
		" 7.82 atm.	132	124	46	335
		" 11.6 atm.	150	140	56	335
616	$C_3H_6O_2$	Methyl acetate	57.1	53.9	17.7	v-l	31, 58
		" 4.4 atm.	107	99	29	335
		" 7.8 atm.	132	120	34.6	335
		" 11.2 atm.	149	135	40.4	335
617	$C_3H_7NO_2$	1-Nitropropane	131.18	Nonazeotrope		55
618	$C_3H_7NO_2$	2-Nitropropane	120.25	Nonazeotrope		55

		B-Component		Azeotropic Data		
No.	Formula	Name	B.P.,°C.	B.P.,°C.	Wt.%A	Ref.
A =	CH$_4$O	**Methanol (continued)**	64.7			
619	C$_3$H$_8$O$_2$	2-Methoxyethanol				
		752 mm.	...	Nonazeotrope	v-l	335
		" 800 mm.	...	Nonazeotrope	v-l	335
620	C$_3$H$_9$BO$_3$	Trimethyl borate	68.0	54.0	27	115, 335
		" 60 p.s.i.g.	...	100	33	335
		" 30 p.s.i.g.	...	84	29	335
		" 200 mm.	...	25	22	335
621	C$_4$H$_6$O$_2$	Vinyl acetate	72.7	58.8	36.6	335
		"	72.6	59.05	36.6	96
622	C$_4$H$_8$O	2-Butanone	79.6	64.5	70	v-l 135
623	C$_4$H$_8$O	Butyraldehyde	74.8	Nonazeotrope		37
624	C$_4$H$_8$O	Tetrahydrofuran,				
		740 mm.	65	59.1	31.1	v-l 115
625	C$_4$H$_8$O$_2$	Ethyl acetate, 40°-60°		% alcohol in-		v-l 228
				creases with		
				pressure		
		"	76.7	62.1	48.6	335
626	C$_4$H$_8$O$_2$	Methyl propionate	79.7	62.0	50	84
627	C$_4$H$_{10}$O	Butyl alcohol, crit.				
		region	117.75	Nonazeotrope	v-l	75, 135
628	C$_4$H$_{11}$N	Diethylamine, 740 mm.	54.7	66.2	40	335
629	C$_5$H$_8$	Isoprene	34.3	29.57	5.2	324
630	C$_5$H$_8$	3-Methyl-1,2-butadiene	40.8	34.7	8.5	324
631	C$_5$H$_8$	cis-1,3-Pentadiene	44.0	38.1	16 vol. %	291
632	C$_5$H$_8$	trans-1,3-Pentadiene	42.0	36.5	15 vol. %	291
		"	...	36.5	12.9	v-l 249
633	C$_5$H$_8$O	1,3-Butadienyl methyl				
		ether	90.7	62	57.5	335
634	C$_5$H$_{10}$	3-Methyl-1-butene	21.2	17.9	4.28	v-l 249
635	C$_5$H$_{10}$	2-Methyl-1-butene	32	27.4	8.1	v-l 249
636	C$_5$H$_{10}$	2-Methyl-2-butene	37.7	33.1	11.2	v-l 249
637	C$_5$H$_{10}$	1-Pentene	29.92	26.4	13 vol. %	291
		"	30.1	26.3	8.92	v-l 249
638	C$_5$H$_{10}$	cis-2-Pentene	37.1	31.8	7 vol. %	291
639	C$_5$H$_{10}$O	2-Pentanone	102.2	Nonazeotrope	v-l	135
640	C$_5$H$_{10}$O$_2$	Isopropyl acetate	88.7	64.0	70.2	335
641	C$_5$H$_{12}$	2-Methylbutane	27.6	24.62	4	324
		"	...	24.2	6.98	v-l 249
642	C$_5$H$_{12}$	Pentane	36.15	30.85	7	324
643	C$_5$H$_{12}$O	Amyl alcohol	137.8	Nonazeotrope	v-l	135
644	C$_5$H$_{12}$O$_2$	2,2-Dimethoxypropane	80	61-62	45	201
645	C$_6$H$_6$	Benzene	80.1	58	38	v-l 182, 275
		" 64.7 p.s.i.a.	108	102	49	v-l 275
		" 112.7 p.s.i.a.	128	123	54	v-l 275
		" 159.7 p.s.i.a.	141	138	58	v-l 275
		" 209.7 p.s.i.a.	152	148	62	v-l 275
		" 259.7 p.s.i.a.	161	159	65	v-l 275
646	C$_6$H$_8$O	2,5-Dimethylfuran	93.3	61.5	51	335
647	C$_6$H$_{10}$	1,3-Hexadiene	72.9	<58	~40	80
648	C$_6$H$_{10}$	2,4-Hexadiene	82	~58	~40	80
649	C$_6$H$_{10}$	3-Methyl-1,3-				
		pentadiene	77	~58	~40	80
650	C$_6$H$_{12}$	Cyclohexane, <760 mm.	...	27.5	34	317
		" <760 mm.	...	30	32.6	317
		" <760 mm.	...	38	31.6	317
		" <760 mm.	...	42	26.8	317
651	C$_6$H$_{12}$	cis-3-Hexene	66.4	49.6	26 vol. %	291
652	C$_6$H$_{12}$O	Butyl vinyl ether	94.2	62	52	335
653	C$_6$H$_{12}$O	4-Methyl-2-pentanone	116.2	Nonazeotrope	v-l	135
654	C$_6$H$_{14}$	2,2-Dimethylbutane	49.74	39.6	17 vol. %	291
655	C$_6$H$_{14}$	2-Methylpentane	60.27	45.6	21 vol. %	291
656	C$_6$H$_{14}$	3-Methylpentane	63.28	47.1	20 vol. %	291

TABLE I   BINARY SYSTEMS   25

		B-Component		Azeotropic Data		
No.	Formula	Name	B.P.,°C.	B.P.,°C.	Wt.%A	Ref.
A =	**CH₄O**	**Methanol (continued)**	**64.7**			
657	C₆H₁₄	Hexane	68.95	49.5	26.4	175
		"	68.95	50.57	28	324
658	C₆H₁₄O	Butyl ethyl ether	92.2	62.6	56	335
659	C₆H₁₄O₂	1,1-Dimethoxybutane	114	Nonazeotrope		334
660	C₆H₁₄O₂	2,2-Dimethoxybutane	106-7	64.5	81.5	201
661	C₇H₈	Toluene	110.7	63.6	70.8 v-1	202
662	C₇H₁₄	trans-1,3-Dimethyl-cyclopentane	90.77	57.3	45 vol. %	291
663	C₇H₁₆	Heptane	98.4	58.8	46.1	174
		" 406 mm.	...	43.83	-	366
664	C₇H₁₆	2-Methylhexane	90.05	57.1	44 vol. %	291
665	C₇H₁₆	3-Methylhexane	91.85	57.6	44 vol. %	291
666	C₇H₁₆	2,2,3-Trimethylbutane	80.88	54.1	38 vol. %	291
667	C₈H₁₀	p-Xylene	138.35	64.0	5	84
668	C₈H₁₄O	2-Ethyl-2-hexenal	176	Nonazeotrope		334
669	C₈H₁₈	Octane	125.75	62.75	67.5	174
		" 406 mm.	...	47.65	-	366
670	C₉H₁₈O	2,6-Dimethyl-4-heptanone	169.4	Nonazeotrope		334
671	C₉H₂₀	Nonane, 406 mm.	...	48.93	-	366
		"	150.7	64.1	83.4	174
672	C₁₀H₂₂	Decane, 406 mm.	...	Nonazeotrope		366
		"	171.8	Nonazeotrope	v-1	249
673	C₁₁H₂₄	Undecane, 406 mm.	...	Nonazeotrope		366
A =	**CH₄S**	**Methanethiol**	**6.00**			
674	C₄H₈	2-Methylpropene, 95 p.s.i.a.	...	53	19.5	145
675	C₄H₁₀	2-Methylpropane	-11.70	-13.00	4.9	21
A =	**CH₅N**	**Methylamine**	**-6**			
676	C₄H₆	Butadiene	...	...	58	20
		" 5 atm.	...	...	74	20
		" 20 atm.	...	...	96	20
677	C₄H₈	1-Butene	...	...	50	20
		" 5 atm.	...	...	64	20
		" 20 atm.	...	...	74	20
A =	**C₂ClF**	**Chloropentafluoro-ethane**	**-38.5**			
678	C₂H₄F₂	1,1-Difluoroethane	-24.7	-41.3	83.8	198
A =	**C₂Cl₂F₄**	**1,2-Dichlorotetra-fluoroethane**	**...**			
679	C₄H₁₀	Butane	-0.5	-2.2	59	102
A =	**C₂Cl₃F₃**	**1,1,2-Trichlorotri-fluoroethane**	**47.5**			
680	C₂Cl₄F₂	1,1,2,2-Tetrachloro-difluoroethane	92.4	Nonazeotrope		96, 334
681	C₂H₆O	Ethyl alcohol	78.3	43.8	96.2	335
A =	**C₂Cl₄**	**Tetrachloroethylene**	**121.1**			
682	C₂H₃Cl₃	1,1,2-Trichloroethane	113.65	112.9	26	197
683	C₃H₆O	Acetone	56.1	Nonazeotrope	v-1	64
684	C₃H₈O	Isopropyl alcohol	82.3	81.7	19	334
685	C₄H₁₀O	Butyl alcohol	117.7	110	68	334
A =	**C₂HCl₃**	**Trichloroethylene**	**86.2**			
686	C₂H₄Cl₂	1,2-Dichloroethane	83.45	82.2	39	197
687	C₂H₄O₂	Acetic acid	117.9	Nonazeotrope		334
688	C₃H₆Cl₂	1,2-Dichloropropane	96.3	Nonazeotrope		334
689	C₄H₈O	2-Butanone	79.6	Nonazeotrope		184
690	C₄H₈O₂	Ethyl acetate, 700-760 mm.	...	Nonazeotrope	v-1	274

		B-Component			Azeotropic Data		
No.	Formula	Name	B.P.,°C.	B.P.,°C.	Wt.%A		Ref.
A =	C_2H_2	Acetylene	-84				
691	C_2H_4	Ethylene	-103.7	...	18		293
		" Crit. press.	...	...	19		293
		" -35°, 0°, 40° F.	...	...	...	v-1	137
692	C_2H_6	Ethane	-88.3	...	39		293
		" Crit. press	...	...	44		293
		" -35°, 0°, 40° F.	...	...	...	v-1	137
693	C_3H_4	Propyne, -50° to 35° C.	...	Nonazeotrope		v-1	28
A =	$C_2H_2Cl_2$	cis-1,2-Dichloro-ethylene	60.3				
694	C_2H_6O	Ethyl alcohol	78.3	Calculated		v-1	5
695	C_3H_6O	Acetone	56.4	61.9	73	v-1	5
696	$C_3H_6O_2$	Ethyl formate	54.0	Nonazeotrope		v-1	5
697	$C_3H_6O_2$	Methyl acetate	57.2	61.7	73	v-1	5
698	$C_3H_8O_2$	Methylal	42.6	Nonazeotrope		v-1	103
699	C_4H_8O	2-Butanone	79.6	Nonazeotrope		v-1	5
700	C_4H_8O	Tetrahydrofuran	66.1	69.8	44.5	v-1	103
701	$C_6H_{14}O$	Isopropyl ether	68.0	Nonazeotrope		v-1	103
A =	$C_2H_2Cl_2$	trans-1,2-Dichloro-ethylene	48.35				
702	C_2H_6O	Ethyl alcohol	78.3	Calculated		v-1	5
703	C_3H_6O	Acetone	56.4	Nonazeotrope		v-1	5
704	$C_3H_6O_2$	Ethyl formate	54.0	Nonazeotrope		v-1	5
705	$C_3H_6O_2$	Methyl acetate	57.2	Nonazeotrope		v-1	5
706	$C_3H_8O_2$	Methylal	42.6	48.6	79.3	v-1	103
707	C_4H_8O	2-Butanone	79.6	Nonazeotrope		v-1	5
708	C_4H_8O	Tetrahydrofuran	66.1	Nonazeotrope		v-1	103
709	$C_6H_{14}O$	Isopropyl ether	68.0	Nonazeotrope		v-1	103
A =	C_2H_3Cl	Vinyl Chloride	13.4				
710	$C_2H_4Cl_2$	1,2-Dichloroethane	83.5	Nonazeotrope			334
711	C_3H_6O	Acetone	56.1	Nonazeotrope			334
A =	$C_2H_3Cl_3$	1,1,1-Trichloroethane	74.1				
712	$C_2H_3Cl_3$	1,1,2-Trichloroethane	113.9	Nonazeotrope			96
713	$C_2H_4Cl_2$	1,1-Dichloroethane	57.4	Nonazeotrope			96
A =	$C_2H_3F_3O$	2,2,2-Trifluoroethanol	...				
714	C_2H_6O	Ethyl alcohol	78.3	81.75	57.65		226
A =	C_2H_3N	Acetonitrile	81.55				
715	$C_2H_4Cl_2$	1,2-Dichloroethane	83.15	~79.1	49	v-1	267
716	C_3H_3N	Acrylonitrile	77.1	Nonazeotrope			334
717	C_3H_6O	Acetone, 45° C.	...	Nonazeotrope		v-1	25
718	C_3H_7NO	N,N-Dimethylform-amide	153	Nonazeotrope			334
		" 100-500 mm.	...	Nonazeotrope			334
719	C_5H_{12}	Pentane, 24 p.s.i.g.	65	58	13		334
720	C_6H_6	Benzene, 278 mm.	...	45	30.7	v-1	22
721	C_6H_7N	2-Picoline	134	Nonazeotrope		v-1	247
722	C_7H_{16}	Heptane	98.4	69.55	...		368
723	C_8H_{18}	Octane	125.75	76.7	...		368
724	C_9H_{20}	Nonane	150.7	79.82	...		368
725	$C_{10}H_{22}$	Decane	173.3	81.45	...		368
726	$C_{11}H_{24}$	Undecane	195.4	Nonazeotrope			368
A =	C_2H_4	Ethylene	-103.7				
727	C_2H_6	Ethane, -35°, 0°, 40° F.	-88.3	...	...	v-1	137
		" 0°, -40°, -100° F.	...	Nonazeotrope		v-1	129
A =	$C_2H_4Br_2$	1,2-Dibromoethane	131.5				
728	C_8H_{10}	m-Xylene	139	Nonazeotrope			113
729	C_8H_{10}	p-Xylene	138.4	131.0	94		113

TABLE I   BINARY SYSTEMS   27

		B-Component		Azeotropic Data		
No.	Formula	Name	B.P.,°C.	B.P.,°C.	Wt.%A	Ref.
A =	$C_2H_4Cl_2$	**1,2-Dichloroethane**	**83.65**			
730	$C_3H_6Cl_2$	1,2-Dichloropropane	96.3	Nonazeotrope		334
731	C_3H_8O	Isopropyl alcohol	82.3	72.7	60.8	334
732	$C_4H_8Cl_2O$	Bis(2-chloroethyl)ether	179.2	Nonazeotrope		334
733	C_6H_6	Benzene	80.1	80.1	15 vol. %	235
734	C_6H_{12}	Cyclohexane	80.75	74.7	38 vol. %	235
735	C_7H_{16}	2,4-Dimethylpentane	80.8	73.7	35 vol. %	235
A =	C_2H_4O	**Acetaldehyde**	**20.2**			
736	C_2H_5Cl	Chloroethane	12.3	11	9.5	96
737	C_3H_6O	Propylene oxide, 35 p.s.i.g.	73	Nonazeotrope		334
738	$C_4H_6O_2$	Vinyl acetate	72.5	Nonazeotrope		96
739	C_4H_8O	Ethyl vinyl ether	35.5	Nonazeotrope		334
740	C_4H_{10}	Butane	-0.5	-7	16	334
741	$C_4H_{10}O$	Ethyl ether	34.5	18.9	76.5	243
742	$C_6H_{14}O$	Isopropyl ether	68.3	Nonazeotrope		334
A =	C_2H_4O	**Ethylene Oxide**	**10.5**			
743	C_4H_{10}	Butane	-0.5	-6.5	22	334
A =	$C_2H_4O_2$	**Acetic Acid**	**118.1**			
744	C_2H_6O	Ethyl alcohol	78.3	Nonazeotrope	v-l	205, 285
745	$C_3H_6O_2$	Propionic acid	140.7	Ideal system	v-l	48
746	C_3H_8O	Propyl alcohol	97.25	Nonazeotrope	v-l	205, 285
747	$C_4H_6O_3$	Acetic anhydride	139.9	Nonazeotrope		334
748	$C_4H_8O_2$	p-Dioxane	...	119.4	79.5	180
749	$C_4H_8O_2$	Ethyl acetate	76.7	Nonazeotrope		334
750	C_4H_9NO	N,N-Dimethyl-acetamide	165	170.8	21.1	295
751	$C_4H_{10}O$	Butyl alcohol	117.1	120.3	43	v-l 205, 285
752	C_5H_5N	Pyridine	115.5	138.1	51.1	373
		" Crit. press.	345	348	20.2	323
753	$C_5H_{10}O_2$	Isopropyl acetate	88.7	Nonazeotrope		334
754	C_5H_{12}	Pentane	36.15	Nonazeotrope		187
755	C_6H_7N	2-Picoline	134	144.12	40.4	369
756	C_6H_{14}	Hexane	68.7	Nonazeotrope		334
		"	68.60	68.25	6.0	187, 189
757	$C_6H_{14}O$	Isopropyl ether	68.3	Nonazeotrope		334
758	C_7H_9	2,6-Lutidine	143.41	147.28	24	v-l 358
		"	144	148.1	22.9	364
		"	...	162.3	19.5	370
759	C_7H_{16}	Heptane	98.25	91.72	33	187, 189, 355, 373
760	C_8H_{10}	o-Xylene	143.6	116.6	78	372
761	C_8H_{18}	Octane	125.75	105.7	53.7	v-l 189, 355, 359
762	C_9H_{12}	Cumene	152.8	116	84	76
763	C_9H_{20}	Nonane	150.2	112.8	69	187, 189, 355
		"	150.2	113.25	69.6	324
764	$C_{10}H_{16}$	Camphene, 100 mm.	...	60.6	90	v-l 294
765	$C_{10}H_{22}$	Decane	173.3	116.75	79.5	187, 189, 355
		"	173.3	117.2	79	324
		"	...	116.10	87	v-l 358
766	$C_{11}H_{24}$	Undecane	194.5	117.72	95	187, 189, 355
		"	194.5	117.17	78	324
767	$C_{12}H_{20}O_2$	Isobornyl acetate	225.8	Ideal system	v-l	294
768	$C_{12}H_{26}$	Dodecane	216	Nonazeotrope		187
A =	C_2H_5Cl	**Chloroethane**	**12.4**			
769	C_4H_{10}	n-Butane	-0.5	...	15.6	255
		" 738.6 mm.	-0.5	-1.4	20.2	v-l 263

		B-Component			Azeotropic Data		
No.	Formula	Name	B.P.,°C.	B.P.,°C.	Wt.%A		Ref.
A =	C$_2$H$_5$ClO	2-Chloroethanol	128.7				
770	C$_4$H$_7$ClO	2-Chloroethyl vinyl ether, 120 mm.	...	55.62	14		341
771	C$_4$H$_8$Cl$_2$O	Bis(2-chloroethyl)ether, 50 mm.	96	Nonazeotrope			334
	"		179.2	Nonazeotrope			334
772	C$_4$H$_8$O$_2$	p-Dioxane	101.3	Nonazeotrope			334
A =	C$_2$H$_5$NO	Acetamide	222				
773	C$_{11}$H$_{10}$	2-Methylnaphthalene	241.1	...	55		98
A =	C$_2$H$_5$NO$_2$	Nitroethane	114.07				
774	C$_2$H$_6$O	Ethyl alcohol	78.32	78.03	12.6		55
775	C$_3$H$_8$O	Isopropyl alcohol	82.40	81.82	10.6		55
776	C$_3$H$_8$O	Propyl alcohol	97.15	94.49	31.8		55
777	C$_4$H$_{10}$O	Butyl alcohol	117.75	107.94	58.6		55
778	C$_4$H$_{10}$O	sec-Butyl alcohol	99.53	97.16	27.6		55
779	C$_4$H$_{10}$O	tert-Butyl alcohol	82.41	82.22	4.5		55
780	C$_4$H$_{10}$O	Isobutyl alcohol	107.89	102.68	40.8		55
A =	C$_2$H$_6$	Ethane					
781	C$_7$F$_{16}$	Perfluoroheptane, crit. region		Nonazeotrope		v-l	155
A =	C$_2$H$_6$O	Ethyl Alcohol	78.3				
782	C$_3$H$_6$O	Acetone	56.4	Nonazeotrope		v-l	7, 134
783	C$_3$H$_7$NO$_2$	1-Nitropropane	131.18	Nonazeotrope			55
784	C$_3$H$_7$NO$_2$	2-Nitropropane	120.25	78.28	93.6		55
785	C$_3$H$_8$O	Isopropyl alcohol	82.3	Nonazeotrope		v-l	116
786	C$_4$H$_8$O	2-Butanone	79.6	74.0	39	v-l	134
	"		79.6	74.8	34		334
787	C$_4$H$_8$O	Butyraldehyde	75.7	70.7	60.6		335
788	C$_4$H$_8$O	Ethyl vinyl ether	35.5	Nonazeotrope			334
789	C$_4$H$_8$O$_2$	p-Dioxane, 200 mm.	...	46.4	68	v-l	124
	"	400 mm.	...	62.4	82		124
	"	600 mm.	...	72.19	88		124
	"	760 mm.	...	78.25	>98		124
790	C$_4$H$_8$O$_2$	Ethyl acetate, 40°-60° C.		% Alc. increases with press.		v-l	228
	"	77.4 mm.	...	...	15.95		117
	"	760 mm.	...	...	30.97		117
	"		77.05	72.18	25.8		228
791	C$_4$H$_{10}$O	Butyl alcohol	117.75	Nonazeotrope		v-l	134
792	C$_4$H$_{10}$O	sec-Butyl alcohol	99.4	Nonazeotrope		v-l	134
793	C$_4$H$_{10}$O$_2$	2-Ethoxyethanol	134	Nonazeotrope		v-l	335
794	C$_4$H$_{11}$N	Butylamine	77.8	82.2	49		335
795	C$_4$H$_{11}$N	Diethylamine	55.5	Nonazeotrope			334
796	C$_5$H$_8$O$_2$	Ethyl acrylate, 100 mm.	44.9	32	54.4		335
797	C$_5$H$_{10}$	2-Methyl-1-butene	31.10	30.1	22 vol. %		291
798	C$_5$H$_{10}$O	Isopropyl vinyl ether, 737 mm.	54.8	52.6	...		334
799	C$_5$H$_{10}$O	2-Pentanone	102.35	78	93.3	v-l	134
800	C$_5$H$_{10}$O	Propyl vinyl ether	65.1	60	18.4		334
801	C$_5$H$_{12}$O	Amyl alcohol	137.8	Nonazeotrope		v-l	134
802	C$_5$H$_{12}$O	Butyl methyl ether	70.3	65.5	20		334
803	C$_5$H$_{12}$O$_2$	2,2-Dimethoxypropane	80	Min. b.p.			201
804	C$_6$H$_6$	Benzene, 310 mm.	...	45	26.2	v-l	22
	"	180 mm.	...	32.5	23.2	v-l	240
	"	400 mm.	...	51.2	28.1	v-l	240
	"	168.4 mm.	...	29.97	21.33	v-l	328
	"	233.5 mm.	...	38.37	23.72		328
	"	336.4 mm.	...	47.15	26.32		328
	"	584 mm.	...	61.06	30.35		328
	"	209 mm.	...	35.0	24.3		256
	"	760 mm.	80.1	67.9	31.7	v-l	191, 344

TABLE 1   BINARY SYSTEMS   **29**

		B-Component		Azeotropic Data		
No.	Formula	Name	B.P.,°C.	B.P.,°C.	Wt.%A	Ref.
A =	C$_2$H$_6$O	Ethyl Alcohol (continued)	78.3			
804	C$_6$H$_6$	Benzene (continued)				
		" 5570 mm.	...	132.9	56	256
		" 11,720 mm.	...	166.9	69.5	256
		" 19,160 mm.	...	191.1	81	256
805	C$_6$H$_7$N	Aniline	184.35	...	... v-l	138
806	C$_6$H$_{10}$	1,3-Hexadiene	72.9	Min. b.p.	...	80
807	C$_6$H$_{10}$	2,4-Hexadiene	82	Min. b.p.		80
808	C$_6$H$_{10}$	3-Methylcyclopentene	64.9	57.2	20 vol. %	291
809	C$_6$H$_{10}$	3-Methyl-1,3-pentadiene	77	Min. b.p.	...	80
810	C$_6$H$_{12}$	Cyclohexane, 296 mm.	...	41.2	25.5	316
		" 420 mm.	...	49.3	27.3	316
		" 643 mm.	...	60.8	29.8	316
		" 760 mm.	...	64.8	31.3	316
		" 760 mm.	80.8	64.9	40	147
811	C$_6$H$_{12}$	2-Ethyl-1-butene	64.95	57.0	23 vol. %	291
812	C$_6$H$_{12}$	1-Hexene	63.49	56.1	22 vol. %	291
813	C$_6$H$_{12}$	cis-2-Hexene	68.8	59.5	22 vol. %	291
814	C$_6$H$_{12}$	cis-3-Hexene	66.4	49.6	26 vol. %	291
815	C$_6$H$_{12}$	Methylcyclopentane	72.0	60.05	22.7 v-l	304
816	C$_6$H$_{12}$	cis-3-Methyl-2-pentene	70.52	60.4	24 vol. %	291
817	C$_6$H$_{12}$	trans-3-Methyl-2-pentene	67.6	58.8	20 vol. %	291
818	C$_6$H$_{12}$	trans-4-Methyl-2-pentene	58.4	52.6	15 vol. %	291
819	C$_6$H$_{12}$O	Butyl vinyl ether	94.2	73	48	335
820	C$_6$H$_{12}$O	Isobutyl vinyl ether	83.4	69.2	33	335
821	C$_6$H$_{12}$O$_3$	Paraldehyde	124.5	Nonazeotrope		334
822	C$_6$H$_{14}$	Hexane	68.95	58	20.8 v-l	304
		" 1545 mm.	...	...	26.3 vol. %	251
823	C$_6$H$_{14}$	2-Methylpentane	60.27	53.1	12 vol. %	291
824	C$_6$H$_{14}$O	Ethyl butyl ether	92.2	73.8	49.3	335
825	C$_6$H$_{14}$O	Isopropyl ether	68.3	64	17.1	335
826	C$_6$H$_{14}$O$_2$	1,2-Diethoxyethane	121.1	Nonazeotrope		334
827	C$_6$H$_{15}$N	Triethylamine	89.7	76.9	51	335
828	C$_7$H$_8$	Toluene	110.7	76.5	66.7 v-l	138, 191
		" 327 mm.	...	...	76.2	117
		" 800 mm.	...	...	81.6	117
829	C$_7$H$_{12}$	1,3-Heptadiene	...	Min. b.p.	...	80
830	C$_7$H$_{12}$	2,4-Heptadiene	...	Min. b.p.	...	80
831	C$_7$H$_{14}$	1,1-Dimethylcyclopentane	87.85	68.0	37 vol. %	291
832	C$_7$H$_{14}$	cis-1,2-Dimethylcyclopentane	99.53	72.1	46 vol. %	291
833	C$_7$H$_{14}$	trans-1,2-Dimethylcyclopentane	91.87	69.6	39 vol. %	291
834	C$_7$H$_{14}$	cis-1,3-Dimethylcyclopentane	91.73	69.5	38 vol. %	291
835	C$_7$H$_{14}$	trans-1,3-Dimethylcyclopentane	90.77	69.1	37 vol. %	291
836	C$_7$H$_{14}$	2,3-Dimethyl-1-pentene	84.2	67.1	35 vol. %	291
837	C$_7$H$_{14}$	Ethylcyclopentane	103.47	73.1	48 vol. %	291
838	C$_7$H$_{14}$	1,1,2,2-Tetramethylcyclopropane	75.9	62.6	30 vol. %	291
839	C$_7$H$_{16}$	2,2-Dimethylpentane	79.20	63.9	25 vol. %	291
840	C$_7$H$_{16}$	2,3-Dimethylpentane	89.78	68.6	34 vol. %	291
841	C$_7$H$_{16}$	2,4-Dimethylpentane	80.50	64.6	29 vol. %	291
842	C$_7$H$_{16}$	3,3-Dimethylpentane	86.07	67.1	38 vol. %	291
843	C$_7$H$_{16}$	3-Ethylpentane	93.47	70	38 vol. %	291
844	C$_7$H$_{16}$	Heptane	98.4	72	48 v-l	138, 239, 335
		" 180 mm.	...	37.5	43 v-l	158

		B-Component			Azeotropic Data		
No.	Formula	Name	B.P.,°C.	B.P.,°C.	Wt.%A		Ref.
A =	C₂H₆O	Ethyl Alcohol (continued)	78.3				
844	C₇H₁₆	Heptane (continued)					
		" 400 mm.	...	54.5	43	v-l	158
		" 750 mm.	...	71.0	45	v-l	158
845	C₇H₁₆	2-Methylhexane	90.05	68.7	36 vol. %		291
846	C₇H₁₆	3-Methylhexane	91.85	69.3	36 vol. %		291
847	C₈H₁₆	1,1-Dimethylcyclo-hexane	119.54	76.2	65 vol. %		291
848	C₈H₁₆	cis-1,4-Dimethyl-cyclohexane	124.32	76.9	70 vol. %		291
849	C₈H₁₆	trans-1,3-Dimethyl-cyclohexane	124.45	76.9	70 vol. %		291
850	C₈H₁₆	trans-1,4-Dimethyl-cyclohexane	119.35	76.2	64 vol. %		291
851	C₈H₁₆	1-Ethyl-1-methyl-cyclopentane	121.52	76.5	66 vol. %		291
852	C₈H₁₆	1,cis-2,trans-3-Trimethylcyclo-pentane	117.5	75.9	62 vol. %		291
853	C₈H₁₆	1,trans-2,cis-4-Trimethylcyclo-pentane	109.29	74.3	52 vol. %		291
854	C₈H₁₆	2,4,4-Trimethyl-2-pentene	104.91	73.9	50 vol. %		291
855	C₈H₁₈	2,2-Dimethylhexane	106.84	73.6	46 vol. %		291
856	C₈H₁₈	2,3-Dimethylhexane	115.61	75.5	57 vol. %		291
857	C₈H₁₈	3,4-Dimethylhexane	117.73	75.8	60 vol. %		291
858	C₈H₁₈	2-Methylheptane	117.65	75.8	59 vol. %		291
859	C₈H₁₈	3-Methylheptane	118.93	76.0	61 vol. %		291
860	C₈H₁₈	4-Methylheptane	117.71	75.8	61 vol. %		291
861	C₈H₁₈	2,2,3-Trimethyl-pentane	109.84	74.3	53 vol. %		291
862	C₈H₁₈	2,2,4-Trimethyl-pentane	99.24	71.8	40 vol. %		291
863	C₈H₁₈	2,3,3-Trimethyl-pentane	114.76	75.3	56 vol. %		291
864	C₈H₁₈	2,3,4-Trimethyl-pentane	113.47	75.1	57 vol. %		291
865	C₈H₁₈O	Butyl ether	142.1	Nonazeotrope			334
866	C₈H₁₈O₂	2-Ethyl-1,3-hexanediol	243.1	Nonazeotrope			334
A =	C₂H₆OS	Dimethylsulfoxide	...				
867	C₆H₆	Benzene, 25°-70°	...	V.p. curve			164
A =	C₂H₆O₂	Ethylene Glycol	197.4				
868	C₃H₄O₃	Ethylene carbonate,					
		10 mm.	...	88	13.9		262
		" 25 mm.	...	107	7.5		262
		" 50 mm.	...	122	2.6		262
		" 72 mm.	...	163	0		262
869	C₄H₈Cl₂O	Bis(2-chloroethyl) ether, 50 mm.	96	92.7	...		335
		"	178.6	164	17.8		60
870	C₄H₈O₂	2-Vinyloxyethanol	143	...	13		94
871	C₄H₈O₃	Ethylene glycol monoacetate	...	Nonazeotrope			147
		" 150 mm.	...	Nonazeotrope			147
872	C₅H₁₂O₃	2-(2-Methoxyethoxy) ethanol	194	...	30		284, 335
		" 50 mm.	115	114	4		335
		" 200 mm.	151	149	12		335
873	C₆H₇N	Aniline, 37.1 mm.	...	95	8.75	v-l	59
		" 104.7 mm.	...	120	12.7	v-l	59
		" 257.9 mm.	...	145	16.8	v-l	59

TABLE I **BINARY SYSTEMS**   **31**

		B-Component		Azeotropic Data		
No.	Formula	Name	B.P.,°C.	B.P.,°C.	Wt.%A	Ref.
A =	$C_2H_6O_2$	**Ethylene Glycol** (continued)	**197.4**			
874	$C_6H_{14}O$	Hexyl alcohol	157.1	Nonazeotrope		334
875	$C_6H_{14}O_3$	2-(2-Ethoxyethoxy) ethanol	202.8	192	45.5	284, 335
		" 100 mm.	137.3	134	33	335
		" 36 mm.	...	108.5	26.6	243
876	C_7H_8	Toluene	110.6	110.1	2.3	335
877	C_7H_8O	Benzyl alcohol	205.2	193.1	56	60
878	C_7H_8O	o-Cresol	191	189.52	26	188
879	C_7H_9N	N̄-Methylaniline, 31.8 mm.	...	95	22.9 v-l	59
		" 95.3 mm.	...	120	26.6 v-l	59
		" 244 mm.	...	145	30.0 v-l	59
880	C_8H_{10}	o-Xylene	144.4	135.7	6.9	335
881	$C_8H_{11}N$	N̄,N-Dimethylaniline, 39.3 mm.	...	95	17.6 v-l	59
		" 115 mm.	...	120	21.8 v-l	59
		" 293 mm.	...	145	26.5 v-l	59
882	$C_8H_{11}N$	s-Collidine	171.3	170.5	9.7	188
883	$C_8H_{18}O$	B̄utyl ether	142.1	139.5	6.4	334, 335
884	$C_8H_{18}O_3$	2-(2-Butoxyethoxy) ethanol	230.6	Min. b.p.		284
885	$C_8H_{19}NO$	2-Diisopropylamino- ethanol, 10 mm.	79	74	10	335
		" 50 mm.	111	104	15	335
		" 100 mm.	127	121	18	335
886	$C_9H_{14}O$	Phorone	197.8	184.5	42	59
887	$C_{10}H_8$	Naphthalene	217.9	183.6	46	147
888	$C_{10}H_{20}OS$	2-Hexylthioethyl vinyl ether	...	Min. b.p.		329
889	$C_{10}H_{22}O_4$	Tripropylene glycol methyl ether	243	192	82 v-l	76
		"	...	138.5	77.2	76
		"	...	111.5	75.1	76
890	$C_{12}H_{10}O$	Phenyl ether, 50 mm.	161.0	120.4	62.3	335
		"	259.3	192.3	64.5	59
891	$C_{12}H_{26}O$	Hexyl ether, 50 mm.	137.0	112.8	35.6	335
892	$C_{14}H_{10}$	Anthracene	340	197	98.3	305
893	$C_{16}H_{34}O$	2-Ethylhexyl ether, 10 mm.	135	87	...	335
A =	C_2H_6S	**Methyl Sulfide**	**37.32**			
894	C_5H_{10}	Cyclopentane	49.35	37.09	87.5	70
895	C_5H_{10}	2-Methyl-2-butene	38.60	34.83	53.6	70
896	C_5H_{10}	2-Methyl-1-butene	31.25	30.64	17.0	70
897	C_5H_{12}	2-Methylbutane	27.90	26.62	25.0	70
898	C_5H_{12}	Pentane	36.15	31.80	46.6	70
899	C_6H_{14}	2,2-Dimethylbutane	49.70	36.50	79.8	70
A =	$C_2H_6S_2$	**Methyl Disulfide**	**109.44**			
900	C_5H_6S	2-Methylthiophene	111.92	Nonazeotrope		70
901	$C_5H_{12}S$	Ethyl isopropyl sulfide	107.22	106.37	...	70
902	C_7H_8	Toluene	110.85	108.93	...	70
903	C_7H_{14}	Methylcyclohexane	101.05	98.92	28.6	70
904	C_7H_{16}	Heptane	98.40	96.44	26.3	70
905	C_8H_{16}	trans-1,3-Dimethyl- cyclohexane	120.30	107.22	73.3	70
906	C_8H_{18}	2,3-Dimethylhexane	109.15	102.84	48.2	70
907	C_8H_{18}	2-Methylheptane	117.70	106.22	69.5	70
A =	C_2H_7N	**Dimethylamine**	**7.4**			
908	$C_4H_{11}NO$	2-(Dimethylamino) ethanol	134.6	Nonazeotrope		334

		B-Component			Azeotropic Data		
No.	Formula	Name	B.P.,°C.	B.P.,°C.	Wt.%A		Ref.
A =	C_2H_7N	**Ethylamine**	**16.6**				
909	$C_4H_{11}N$	Diethylamine	55.5	Nonazeotrope			334
910	$C_4H_{11}NO_2$	2,2'-Iminodiethanol	...	Nonazeotrope			334
A =	C_2H_7NO	**2-Aminoethanol**	**171.0**				
911	C_3H_6O	Acetone	56.1	Nonazeotrope			334
912	$C_4H_{11}NO_2$	2,2'-Iminodiethanol, 10 mm.	150	Nonazeotrope			334
A =	$C_2H_8N_2$	**Ethylenediamine**	**116.9**				
913	$C_4H_8O_2$	p-Dioxane	101.3	Nonazeotrope			334
914	$C_4H_{10}O$	Butyl alcohol	117.7	124.7	35.7		335
915	$C_4H_{10}O$	Isobutyl alcohol	107.9	120.5	50		335
916	C_6H_6	Benzene	80.1	Nonazeotrope			334
917	C_7H_8	Toluene	110.7	104	30.8		76
		"	...	103	30		334
A =	$C_3HF_5O_2$	**Pentafluoropropionic Acid**	...				
918	C_6F_{14}	Perfluorohexane, 25° C.	...	Nonazeotrope		v-1	237
A =	$C_3H_2ClF_3O_2$	**3-Chloro-2,2,3-trifluoropropionic Acid**	...				
919	C_3H_7NO	N,N,-Dimethylformamide, 20 mm.	...	115-120	...		93
A =	$C_3H_2F_4O_2$	**2,2,3,3-Tetrafluoropropionic Acid**	...				
920	C_3H_7NO	N,N-Dimethylformamide, 20 mm.	...	40	67		93
A =	$C_3H_3ClF_3NO$	**3-Chloro-2,2,3-trifluoropropionamide**	...				
921	C_3H_7NO	N,N-Dimethylformamide, 20 mm.	...	101-106	...		93
A =	$C_3H_3F_4NO$	**2,2,3,3-Tetrafluoropropionamide**	...				
922	C_3H_7NO	N,N-Dimethylformamide, 20 mm.	...	91-4	66		93
		"	153	187	...		93
A =	C_3H_3N	**Acrylonitrile**	**77.2**				
923	C_3H_5N	Propionitrile	97.4	Nonazeotrope			334
A =	C_3H_4	**Propadiene**	**-32**				
924	C_3H_4	Propyne	-23.2	Nonazeotrope			334
925	C_3H_6	Propene	-47.7	Nonazeotrope			334
926	C_3H_8	Propane	-42.1	-42	11.6 vol. %		334
927	C_4H_6	1,3-Butadiene	-4.5	Nonazeotrope			334
A =	C_3H_4	**Propyne**	**-23.2**				
928	C_3H_6	Propene	-47.7	Nonazeotrope			334
929	C_3H_8	Propane	-42.1	-42	11.7 vol. %		334
930	C_4H_6	1,3-Butadiene	-4.5	Nonazeotrope			334
A =	$C_3H_4Cl_4$	**Tetrachloropropane**	...				
931	$C_5H_8Cl_4$	Tetrachloropentane, 12-150 mm.	...	Nonazeotrope		v-1	250
A =	C_3H_4O	**2-Propyn-1-ol**	**115**				
932	C_6H_6	Benzene	80.1	78	9		95
A =	$C_3H_4O_2$	**Acrylic Acid**	**141.2**				
933	$C_5H_8O_2$	Ethyl acrylate	99.3	Nonazeotrope			334

TABLE I   BINARY SYSTEMS   **33**

		B-Component			Azeotropic Data		
No.	Formula	Name	B.P.,°C.	B.P.,°C.	Wt.%A		Ref.
A =	C_3H_5Cl	3-Chloropropene	45.15				
934	C_3H_7Cl	2-Chloropropane	34.9	Nonazeotrope		v-l	83
A =	C_3H_5ClO	2-Chloro-2-propen-1-ol	...				
935	C_5H_7ClO	2-Chloroallyl vinyl ether	...	...	10		341
A =	C_3H_5ClO	Epichlorohydrin	116.45				
936	$C_3H_5Cl_3$	1,2,3-Trichloropropane	156.85	Nonazeotrope		v-l	337
A =	C_3H_6	Propene	-48				
937	C_3H_8	Propane, 10°--190° F.	...	Nonazeotrope		v-l	128
A =	$C_3H_6Cl_2$	1,2-Dichloropropane	96.3				
938	C_3H_6O	Propylene oxide, 20 p.s.i.g.	60	Nonazeotrope			334
939	$C_3H_8O_2$	1,2-Propanediol	187.3	Nonazeotrope			334
A =	C_3H_6O	Acetone	56.5				
940	C_3H_8O	Isopropyl alcohol	82.3	Nonazeotrope		v-l	45, 46
941	$C_4H_4O_2$	Diketene	...	Nonazeotrope			334
942	$C_4H_6O_2$	Vinyl acetate	72.7	Nonazeotrope			334
943	C_4H_7Cl	1-Chloro-2-methyl-propene	68	55.6	81		241
944	C_4H_8O	2-Butanone, 15-500 p.s.i.a.	...	Nonazeotrope		v-l	254, 334
945	$C_5H_8O_2$	Isopropenyl acetate	96.5	Nonazeotrope			147
946	C_5H_{10}	1-Pentene	29.97	28.9	19 vol. %		291
947	$C_5H_{10}O_2$	Isopropyl acetate	88.7	Nonazeotrope			334
948	C_5H_{12}	Pentane	36.15	32.5	20		131
		" <100 mm.	...	Nonazeotrope			131
949	C_6H_6	Benzene, 45° C.	...	Nonazeotrope		v-l	23
		"	80.1	Nonazeotrope		v-l	36
950	C_6H_{12}	Cyclohexane	80.75	53.0	67.5	v-l	186
		"	80.75	...	67		256
951	C_6H_{12}	Methylcyclopentane	72.0	...	57		256
952	C_6H_{12}	1,1,2-Trimethyl-cyclopropane	52.6	42.3	32 vol. %		291
953	$C_6H_{12}O$	4-Methyl-2-pentanone	115.9	Nonazeotrope		v-l	157
954	$C_6H_{12}O_2$	Butyl acetate	126.2	Nonazeotrope		v-l	63
955	C_6H_{14}	2,3-Dimethylbutane	58.0	...	46.5		256
956	C_6H_{14}	Hexane	68.95	49.8	59		256, 334
957	C_7H_{16}	Heptane	98.4	...	89.5		256
A =	C_3H_6O	Allyl Alcohol	96.6				
958	C_3H_8O	Isopropyl alcohol	82.3	Nonazeotrope		v-l	172
959	C_5H_8O	Allyl vinyl ether	...	...	10		341
		"	67.4	66.6	5		334
960	$C_5H_8O_2$	Allyl acetate	...	95.1	63		1
961	C_6H_{12}	Cyclohexane	80.8	74.0	58		147
962	C_6H_{14}	Hexane	68.8	...	12.5		176
963	$C_6H_{14}O$	Isopropyl ether	68.3	Nonazeotrope			334
A =	C_3H_6O	Propionaldehyde	48.7				
964	C_3H_6O	Propylene oxide, 30 p.s.i.g.	69	Nonazeotrope			334
965	C_5H_6O	2-Methylfuran	63.7	Nonazeotrope			270
A =	C_3H_6O	Propylene Oxide	35				
966	$C_4H_{10}O$	Ethyl ether	34.5	32.6	49.6		243
A =	$C_3H_6O_2$	1,3-Dioxolane	75.6				
967	C_7H_8	Toluene	110.6	Nonazeotrope			334
968	C_7H_{16}	Heptane	98.4	72.3	81		334

		B-Component		Azeotropic Data		
No.	Formula	Name	B.P.,°C.	B.P.,°C.	Wt.%A	Ref.
A =	C₃H₆O₂	1,3-Dioxolane (continued)	75.6			
969	C₈H₁₈O	Butyl ether	142.1	Nonazeotrope		334
970	C₉H₂₀	Nonane	150.8	Nonazeotrope		334
A =	C₃H₆O₂	Ethyl Formate	54.1			
971	C₃H₇Br	2-Bromopropane	59.35	53.0	59.4	195, 252
A =	C₃H₆O₂	Methyl Acetate	56.95			
972	C₃H₇Br	2-Bromopropane	59.35	55.6	14.5	195
973	C₅H₆O	2-Methylfuran	...	Nonazeotrope		270
974	C₅H₈	Cyclopentene	44.4	41.7	27.7	126
975	C₅H₁₀	Cyclopentane	49.3	43.2	37.9	126
976	C₅H₁₀	1-Pentene	30.1	30.0	3.3	126
977	C₅H₁₂	Pentane	36.08	34.05	22	126
978	C₆H₆	Benzene	80.1	56.7	99.7	126
979	C₆H₈	1,3-Cyclohexadiene	80.25	56.7	98.0	126
980	C₆H₁₀	Cyclohexene	83.1	56.5	90.2	126
981	C₆H₁₂	Cyclohexane	80.6	54.9	83.0	126
982	C₆H₁₂	2,3-Dimethyl-1-butene	55.62	48.95	42.8	126
983	C₆H₁₂	2,3-Dimethyl-2-butene	73.38	55.1	71.8	126
984	C₆H₁₂	3,3-Dimethyl-1-butene	41.4	39.9	8.8	126
985	C₆H₁₂	2-Ethyl-1-butene	64.8	52.8	60.1	126
986	C₆H₁₂	1-Hexene	63.58	52.5	63.6	126
987	C₆H₁₂	cis-2-Hexene	68.55	53.7	69.8	126
988	C₆H₁₂	3-Methyl-2-pentene	70.64	54.45	73.7	126
989	C₆H₁₂	4-Methyl-1-pentene	54.0	48.3	36.7	126
990	C₆H₁₂	trans-4-Methyl-2-pentene	58.45	50.0	51.3	126
991	C₆H₁₂	Methylcyclopentane	71.8	53.0	68.0	126
992	C₆H₁₄	2,2-Dimethylbutane	49.65	43.7	38.2	126
993	C₆H₁₄	2,3-Dimethylbutane	58.05	48.0	48.25	126
994	C₆H₁₄	Hexane	68.85	51.75	60.7	126
995	C₆H₁₄	2-Methylpentane	60.2	49.25	51.6	126
996	C₆H₁₄	3-Methylpentane	63.25	50.05	57.4	126
997	C₇H₁₆	2,4-Dimethylpentane	80.7	54.7	72.4	126
998	C₇H₁₆	Heptane	98.45	56.65	96.45	126
999	C₇H₁₆	2-Methylhexane	90.0	56.0	88.6	126
1000	C₇H₁₆	3-Methylhexane	91.85	56.3	84.9	126
1001	C₇H₁₆	2,2,3-Trimethylbutane	80.9	55.1	74.2	126
A =	C₃H₆O₂	Propionic Acid	140.7			
1002	C₄H₆O₃	Acetic anhydride	138	Nonazeotrope	v-l	250
1003	C₅H₅N	Pyridine	115.5	148.6	67.2	370
1004	C₅H₁₁NO	N,N-Dimethylpropionamide	175.5	179.3	23.6	295
1005	C₆H₁₄	Hexane	68.85	Nonazeotrope		189
1006	C₇H₁₆	Heptane	98.15	97.82	2.0	189
1007	C₈H₁₈	Octane	125.12	120.89	24	189
		"	125.12	...	24.2	v-l 154
		" Satd. with Na propionate	...	...	6	v-l 154
1008	C₉H₂₀	Nonane	150.67	134.27	54	189
1009	C₁₀H₂₂	Decane	174.06	139.76	80.5	189
1010	C₁₁H₂₄	Undecane	193.85	Nonazeotrope		189
A =	C₃H₆O₃	Methyl Glycolate	151.2			
1011	C₈H₁₀	Ethylbenzene	136.15	Min. b.p.	...	52
1012	C₈H₁₀	m-Xylene	139	Min. b.p.	...	52
A =	C₃H₆O₃	s-Trioxane	114.5			
1013	C₆H₁₂	Cyclohexane	80.75	Min. b.p.	...	52
A =	C₃H₇ClO	Propylene Chlorohydrin	73/100			
1014	C₆H₁₂Cl₂O	Bis(chloroisopropyl) ether, 100 mm.	121.9	Nonazeotrope		334

TABLE I *BINARY SYSTEMS* **35**

		B-Component		Azeotropic Data			
No.	Formula	Name	B.P.,°C.	B.P.,°C.	Wt.%A		Ref.
A =	C₃H₇NO	N,N-Dimethylformamide	153				
1015	C₆H₆	Benzene	80.1	Nonazeotrope			52
A =	C₃H₇NO	Propionamide	222.1				
1016	C₁₀H₂₂	Decane, 50 mm.	...	88	3		26
		" 100 mm.	...	106	5		26
		" 200 mm.	...	126	7.5		26
		" 760 mm.	173.3	168	11.8		26
1017	C₁₁H₂₄	Undecane, 50 mm.	...	105	15		26
		" 100 mm.	...	123	16		26
		" 200 mm.	...	142	17.3		26
		" 760 mm.	194.5	183	21		26
1018	C₁₂H₂₆	Dodecane, 50 mm.	...	115	26		26
		" 100 mm.	...	132	26		26
		" 200 mm.	...	152	26		26
		" 760 mm.	216	193	31.6		26
A =	C₃H₇NO₂	1-Nitropropane	131.18				
1019	C₃H₈O	Isopropyl alcohol	82.40	Nonazeotrope			55
1020	C₃H₈O	Propyl alcohol	97.15	96.95	8.8		55
1021	C₄H₁₀O	Butyl alcohol	117.73	115.30	32.2		55
1022	C₄H₁₀O	sec-Butyl alcohol	99.53	99.40	4.1		55
1023	C₄H₁₀O	tert-Butyl alcohol	82.41	Nonazeotrope			55
1024	C₄H₁₀O	Isobutyl alcohol	107.89	105.28	15.2		55
A =	C₃H₇NO₂	2-Nitropropane	120.25				
1025	C₃H₈O	Isopropyl alcohol	82.40	82.24	4.2		55
1026	C₃H₈O	Propyl alcohol	97.15	95.97	24.9		55
1027	C₄H₁₀O	Butyl alcohol	117.73	111.61	52.4		55
1028	C₄H₁₀O	sec-Butyl alcohol	99.53	98.70	18.0		55
1029	C₄H₁₀O	tert-Butyl alcohol	82.41	Nonazeotrope			55
1030	C₄H₁₀O	Isobutyl alcohol	107.89	105.28	33.1		55
A =	C₃H₈O	Isopropyl Alcohol	82.3				
1031	C₄H₆O₂	Vinyl acetate	72.7	70.8	22.4		335
1032	C₄H₈O₂	p-Dioxane	...	...	...	v-l	47
1033	C₄H₈O₂	Ethyl acetate	77.05	75.9	25	v-l	228
		" 40°-60° C.	...	...		v-l	228
1034	C₄H₈O₂	Methyl propionate	79.6	77	28		335
1035	C₄H₉Cl	1-Chloro-2-methyl-propane	68.9	63.8	19		335
1036	C₄H₁₀O	Ethyl ether	34.6	Nonazeotrope			334
1037	C₄H₁₁N	Butylamine	77.8	84.7	60		335
1038	C₅H₁₀O	Isopropyl vinyl ether	...	...	16.5		341
1039	C₅H₁₀O	2-Pentanone	102.35	Nonazeotrope		v-l	11
1040	C₆H₆	Benzene, 155 mm.	...	31.8	20.6		316
		" 243 mm.	...	41.8	23.6		316
		" 509 mm.	...	60.4	29.9		316
		" 607 mm.	...	65.3	31.4		316
		" 760 mm.	...	71.74	33.7		316
		" 196 mm.	...	37.2	22.4		256
		" 512 mm.	...	60.3	30		256
		" 4920 mm.	...	134.7	62		256
		" 10,180 mm.	...	166.3	79		256
		" 15,380 mm.	...	186.1	91		256
1041	C₆H₁₀	1,3-Hexadiene	72.9	Min. b.p.			80
1042	C₆H₁₀	2,4-Hexadiene	82	Min. b.p.			80
1043	C₆H₁₀	3-Methyl-1,3-pentadiene	77	Min. b.p.			80
1044	C₆H₁₀O	Mesityl oxide	128.3	Nonazeotrope			334
1045	C₆H₁₂	Cyclohexane, 129 mm.	...	26.3	18.3		316
		" 270 mm.	...	42.5	23.3		316
		" 434 mm.	...	54.1	27.1		316
		" 549 mm.	...	60.2	29.2		316
		" 760 mm.	...	69.4	32		316
1046	C₆H₁₂O	4-Methyl-2-pentanone	115.9	Nonazeotrope			11
1047	C₆H₁₅N	Diisopropylamine	84.1	79.7	40		335

		B-Component			Azeotropic Data	
No.	Formula	Name	B.P.,°C.	B.P.,°C.	Wt.%A	Ref.
A =	C_3H_8O	Isopropyl Alcohol (continued)	82.3			
1048	$C_6H_{15}N$	Hexylamine	132.7	Nonazeotrope		334
1049	C_7H_8	Toluene	110.7	. . .	52	327
		"	110.6	80.6	69	335
1050	C_8H_{14}	Diisobutylene	102.3	77.8	54.5	335
1051	C_8H_{16}	trans-1,2-Dimethyl-cyclohexane	123.42	81.4	79 vol. %	291
1052	C_8H_{16}	cis-1-Ethyl-2-methyl-cyclopentane	128.05	82.2	83 vol. %	291
1053	C_8H_{16}	trans-1-Ethyl-2-methylcyclopentane	121.2	81.6	76 vol. %	291
1054	C_8H_{16}	trans-1-Ethyl-3-methylcyclopentane	120.8	81.4	75 vol. %	291
1055	C_8H_{16}	1,1,2-Trimethyl-cyclopentane	113.73	80.4	66 vol. %	291
1056	C_8H_{16}	1,1,3-Trimethyl-cyclopentane	104.89	78.5	53 vol. %	291
1057	C_8H_{16}	1,cis-2,trans-3-Trimethylcyclo-pentane	117.5	81.1	71 vol. %	291
1058	C_8H_{16}	1,cis-2,trans-4-Trimethylcyclo-pentane	116.73	80.9	71 vol. %	291
1059	C_8H_{18}	2,2,4-Trimethyl-pentane	99.3	77.3	48.5 v-l	29
A =	C_3H_8O	Propyl Alcohol	97.25			
1060	C_3H_8S	1-Propanethiol, 766 mm.	67.8	66.4	8.65	181
1061	$C_4H_8O_2$	Ethyl acetate, 40°-60° C.	77.05	Nonazeotrope	v-l	228
1062	$C_5H_{10}O$	3-Pentanone	101.8	94.9	57	334
1063	$C_5H_{10}O_2$	Propyl acetate	101.6	94.7	49 v-l	264
		" 200 mm.	. . .	59.96	31.4 v-l	306
		" 400 mm.	. . .	77.06	39.2 v-l	306
		" 600 mm.	. . .	88.04	44.8 v-l	306
		" 760 mm.	. . .	94.7	48.9 v-l	306
1064	C_6H_5Cl	Chlorobenzene	132	96.5	80	334
1065	C_6H_6	Benzene, 239 mm.	. . .	45	10.5 v-l	24
		" 44.7-309.7 p.s.i.g.	. . .	Effect of press.	v-l	277
		" 123 mm.	. . .	28.0	8.0	316, 344
		" 289 mm.	. . .	49.8	11.6	316, 344
		" 423 mm.	. . .	59.9	13.6	316, 344
		" 610 mm.	. . .	70.1	15.7	316, 344
		" 760 mm.	. . .	77.10	17.1	316, 344
		" 342 mm.	. . .	53.7	12.3	256
		" 573 mm.	. . .	68.6	15.3	256
		" 2420 mm.	. . .	117.6	27.5	256
		" 5020 mm.	. . .	147.5	37	256
		" 10,050 mm.	. . .	183.8	50.5	256
		" 18,200 mm.	. . .	218.3	66.1	256
1066	C_6H_{12}	Cyclohexane, 161 mm.	. . .	33.8	9.9	316
		" 250 mm.	. . .	44.3	11.8	316
		" 429 mm.	. . .	58.0	15.0	316
		" 560 mm.	. . .	65.4	16.5	316
		" 760 mm.	. . .	74.69	18.5	316
		" 4-15 atm.	. . .	Effect of press.		278
1067	$C_6H_{12}O$	2-Methylpentanal	118.3	95	86	334
1068	$C_6H_{16}OSi$	(Trimethylsiloxy)propane, 735 mm.	100.3	87.5	. . .	193
1069	C_7H_8	Toluene	110.7	. . .	50.5	327
		"	110.6	92.6	49	334
		"	110.7	92.6	51.5 v-l	202
1070	C_8H_8	Styrene, 50 mm.	. . .	38.5	84 v-l	211
		"	. . .	% PrOH increases with press.		211

TABLE I **BINARY SYSTEMS** 37

		B-Component		Azeotropic Data		
No.	Formula	Name	B.P.,°C.	B.P.,°C.	Wt.%A	Ref.
A =	C_3H_8O	Propyl Alcohol (continued)	97.25			
1071	C_8H_{10}	Ethylbenzene, 50 mm.	...	% PrOH increases with press.		211
1072	C_8H_{10}	p-Xylene	138.4	...	92	327
A =	C_3H_8OS	2-(Methylthio)ethanol	...			
1073	$C_5H_{10}OS$	2-Methylthioethyl vinyl ether, 22 mm.	...	75	20	329
A =	$C_3H_8O_2$	2-Methoxyethanol	124.5			
1074	C_6H_6	Benzene	80.1	Nonazeotrope	v-l	331
1075	C_6H_{12}	Cyclohexane	80.7	Nonazeotrope		334
		"	...	77.5	15	v-l	331
1076	C_7H_{14}	trans-2-Heptene	98.0	92.9	19 vol. %	291
1077	$C_7H_{16}O_2$	1-tert-Butoxy-2-methoxyethane	...	119	45	76
1078	C_8H_8	Styrene, 57 mm.	67.9	54.8	62 vol. %	291
		" 62 mm.	...	56.8	50.1	v-l	152
1079	C_8H_{10}	Ethylbenzene, 62 mm.	...	51.9	34.3	v-l	152
1080	C_8H_{10}	p-Xylene	138.35	119.3	54 vol. %	291
1081	C_8H_{12}	4-Vinylcyclohexene, 57 mm.	...	44.4	30 vol. %	291
1082	C_8H_{16}	cis-1,3-Dimethyl-cyclohexane	120.9	105.6	36 vol. %	291
1083	C_8H_{16}	trans-1-Ethyl-2-methylcyclopentane	121.2	106.3	32 vol. %	291
1084	C_8H_{16}	trans-1-Ethyl-3-methylcyclopentane	120.8	106.0	35 vol. %	291
1085	C_8H_{16}	1,1,3-Trimethyl-cyclopentane	104.89	96.7	20 vol. %	291
1086	C_8H_{16}	1,cis-2,cis-3-Tri-methylcyclopentane	123.0	107.4	35 vol. %	291
1087	C_8H_{16}	1,trans-2,cis-3-Tri-methylcyclopentane	110.2	100.2	20 vol. %	291
1088	C_8H_{16}	2,4,4-Trimethyl-1-pentene	101.44	95.5	20 vol. %	291
1089	C_8H_{18}	2,4-Dimethylhexane	109.43	99.3	26 vol. %	291
1090	C_8H_{18}	2,2,3-Trimethylpentane	109.84	99.7	25 vol. %	291
1091	C_9H_{18}	1,1,3-Trimethyl-cyclohexane	136.6	113.1	41 vol. %	291
1092	C_9H_{20}	2,2,3,4-Tetramethyl-pentane	133.02	111.4	39 vol. %	291
1093	C_9H_{20}	2,3,4-Trimethylhexane	139.0	113.5	39 vol. %	291
1094	C_9H_{20}	2,3,5-Trimethylhexane	131.34	110.6	40 vol. %	291
A =	$C_3H_8O_2$	1,2-Propanediol	187.8			
1095	$C_5H_{10}O_2$	3-Vinyloxypropanol	...	Min. b.p.		94
1096	C_6H_6	Benzene	80.1	Nonazeotrope		334
1097	$C_6H_{14}O_3$	Dipropylene glycol, 10 mm.	...	Nonazeotrope	v-l	60
1098	C_7H_8	Toluene	110.6	110.5	1.5	335
1099	C_8H_6O	Coumarone	173	Azeo. distillation		120
1100	C_8H_{10}	o-Xylene	144.4	135.8	10	335
1101	$C_8H_{18}O$	Butyl ether	142.1	136	...	334, 335
1102	$C_{10}H_8$	Naphthalene	218.1	Azeo. distillation		120
1103	$C_{10}H_{22}O_4$	Tripropylene glycol methyl ether, 50 mm.	...	Nonazeotrope		76
1104	$C_{12}H_{26}$	Dodecane	216	175	67	60
1105	$C_{14}H_{30}$	Tetradecane	252.5	179	76	60
1106	$C_{16}H_{34}O$	Bis(2-ethylhexyl) ether, 10 mm.	135	84	...	335
A =	$C_3H_8O_2$	1,3-Propanediol	214			
1107	$C_5H_{10}O_2$	3-Vinyloxy-1-propanol	...	...	10-15	94

		B-Component		Azeotropic Data		
No.	Formula	Name	B.P.,°C.	B.P.,°C.	Wt.%A	Ref.
A =	C₃H₈S	**Ethyl Methyl Sulfide**	**66.61**			
1108	C₆H₁₂	Cyclohexane	80.35	Nonazeotrope		70
1109	C₆H₁₂	1-Hexene	63.50	62.71	29.4	70
1110	C₆H₁₂	Methylcyclopentane	71.85	65.59	64.1	70
1111	C₆H₁₄	2,3-Dimethylbutane	58.10	57.41	18.7	70
1112	C₆H₁₄	Hexane	68.75	63.94	56.6	70
1113	C₇H₁₆	2,2-Dimethylpentane	79.20	66.37	88.2	70
A =	C₃H₉BO₃	**Trimethyl Borate**	**68.7**			
1114	C₄H₈O	Tetrahydrofuran	65	Nonazeotrope	v-l	115
A =	C₃H₉N	**Isopropylamine**	**32.4**			
1115	C₆H₁₄	Hexane	68.7	Nonazeotrope		334
A =	C₃H₉NO	**1-Amino-2-propanol**	**159.9**			
1116	C₆H₅Cl	Chlorobenzene	131	128.30	13	259
1117	C₆H₁₅NO₂	1,1'-Iminodi-2-				
		propanol, 100 mm.	185	Nonazeotrope		334
1118	C₇H₈	Toluene	110.7	110	5	259
1119	C₇H₁₆	Heptane	98.4	96.6	6	334
A =	C₃H₁₀N₂	**1,2-Propanediamine**	**120.9**			
1120	C₄H₁₀O	Butyl alcohol	117.7	126.5	49	335
1121	C₄H₁₀O	Isobutyl alcohol	107.9	123	65	335
1122	C₇H₈	Toluene	110.6	105	32	334
A =	C₄Cl₃F₇	**2,2,3-Trichloro-**	**97.4**			
		heptafluorobutane				
1123	C₅Cl₂F₆	1,2-Dichlorohexa-				
		fluorocyclopentene	90.6	Nonazeotrope	v-l	354
1124	C₇H₁₆	Heptane	98.53	92.3	76	v-l	354
1125	C₈F₁₆O	Perfluorocyclic oxide	102.6	96.35	67	v-l	354
A =	C₄HF₇O₂	**Perfluorobutyric Acid**	**122.0**			
1126	C₈H₁₀	Ethylbenzene	136.15	115.4	80	52
1127	C₈H₁₀	m-Xylene	139	117.5	83	52
1128	C₈H₁₀	p̲-Xylene	138.4	117.6	82	52
A =	C₄H₂O₃	**Maleic Anhydride**	...			
1129	C₈H₁₀	m-Xylene, 150 mm.	...	Nonazeotrope		334
1130	C₁₆H₂₂O₄	D̲ibutyl phthalate,				
		50 mm.	238	Nonazeotrope		334
A =	C₄H₄	**Vinylacetylene**	...			
1131	C₄H₅Cl	2-Chloro-1,3-				
		butadiene, 740 mm.	...	Nonazeotrope	v-l	151
A =	C₄H₄O₂	**Diketene**	...			
1132	C₇H₈	Toluene, 60 mm.	...	41	10	84
A =	C₄H₄S	**Thiophene**	**83.97**			
1133	C₄H₁₀S	2-Butanethiol	85.15	82.27	...	70
1134	C₄H₁₀S	Isopropyl methyl				
		sulfide	84.76	83.42	...	70
1135	C₆H₆	Benzene	80.10	Nonazeotrope		70
1136	C₆H₁₂	Cyclohexane	80.85	77.90	41.2	70
1137	C₆H₁₂	Methylcyclopentane	71.85	71.47	14.0	70
1138	C₆H₁₄	Hexane	68.75	68.46	11.2	70
1139	C₇H₁₄	trans-1,3-Dimethyl-				
		cyclopentane	90.80	82.00	67.7	70
1140	C₇H₁₆	2,3-Dimethylpentane	89.90	80.90	64	70
1141	C₇H₁₆	2,4-Dimethylpentane	80.55	76.58	42.7	70
1142	C₇H₁₆	Heptane	98.40	83.09	83.2	70

TABLE I BINARY SYSTEMS   **39**

		B-Component		Azeotropic Data		
No.	Formula	Name	B.P.,°C.	B.P.,°C.	Wt.%A	Ref.
A =	C_4H_5Cl	2-Chloro-1,3-butadiene	...			
1143	$C_4H_6Cl_2$	1,3-Dichloro-2-butene,				
		100 mm.	...	Nonazeotrope	v-l	151
		" 340 mm.	...	Nonazeotrope	v-l	151
1144	C_4H_6O	3-Butene-2-one,				
		100 mm.	...	Nonazeotrope	v-l	151
		" 340 mm.	...	Nonazeotrope	v-l	151
A =	$C_4H_6O_2$	2,3-Butanedione	90.7			
1145	C_4H_8O	2-Butanone	79.6	Nonazeotrope		334
A =	$C_4H_6O_2$	Vinyl Acetate	72.7			
1146	$C_4H_{10}O$	Butyl alcohol	117.7	Nonazeotrope		334
1147	C_6H_{12}	Cyclohexane	80.7	67.4	61.3	334
1148	C_7H_{16}	Heptane	98.4	72	83.5	334
1149	$C_8H_{18}O$	Butyl ether	142.1	Nonazeotrope		334
A =	$C_4H_6O_3$	Acetic Anhydride	139.9			
1150	$C_5H_8O_2$	Isopropenyl acetate	97.4	Nonazeotrope		334
1151	$C_5H_{10}O_2$	Isopropyl acetate	88.7	Nonazeotrope		334
1152	$C_6H_{14}O$	Isopropyl ether	68.3	Nonazeotrope		334
A =	C_4H_7ClO	2-Chloroethyl Vinyl Ether	109.1			
1153	$C_5H_{12}O$	Isoamyl alcohol	131.8	109	99	335
		" 50 mm.	67	39	99	335
A =	$C_4H_8Cl_2O$	Bis(2-chloroethyl Ether)	178.65			
1154	$C_4H_{10}O_3$	Diethylene glycol	245.5	174.6	92	60
1155	$C_7H_{16}O$	3-Heptanol	156.4	141.2	28	334
1156	$C_8H_{18}O$	2-Ethyl-1-hexanol, 50 mm.	109	96	90	335
A =	C_4H_8O	2-Butanone	79.6			
1157	$C_4H_8O_2$	Isopropyl formate	68.8	Nonazeotrope		310
1158	C_4H_9Cl	1-Chloro-2-methyl-propane	68.8	Nonazeotrope		310
1159	$C_4H_{10}O$	sec-Butyl alcohol	99.5	Nonazeotrope	v-l	8
		" 374 mm.	...	Nonazeotrope	v-l	8
1160	C_5H_6O	2-Methylfuran	...	Nonazeotrope	v-l	310
1161	C_6H_6	Benzene	80.1	78.1	47	v-l	74
		" 14.7 p.s.i.a.	...	78.2	45	v-l	321
		" 66.7 p.s.i.a.	...	133.0	67.6	v-l	321
		" 118.0 p.s.i.a.	...	160.7	90.0	v-l	321
		" 125.0 p.s.i.a.	...	Nonazeotrope	v-l	321
1162	C_6H_6O	Phenol, 200-760 mm.	...	Nonazeotrope	v-l	33
1163	C_6H_8O	2,5-Dimethylfuran	93.3	Nonazeotrope		334
1164	C_6H_{12}	Cyclohexane,				
		" 14.7 p.s.i.a.	...	71.0	52.5	321
		" 66.7 p.s.i.a.	...	128.7	61.0	321
		" 118.0 p.s.i.a.	...	156.4	64.0	321
		" 125.0 p.s.i.a.	...	182.5	69.0	321
		"	80.85	71.6	45.5	186
		"	80.85	71.5	44	73
		"	80.85	...	42	256
1165	C_6H_{14}	2,3-Dimethylbutane	58	...	15.1	256
1166	C_6H_{14}	Hexane	68.95	...	29.6	256
1167	C_7H_{14}	Methylcyclohexane	101.15	...	80	256
1168	C_7H_{16}	Heptane	98.4	...	73	256
1169	C_8H_{18}	2,5-Dimethylhexane	109.4	...	95	256
A =	C_4H_8O	Butyraldehyde	74.8			
1170	C_4H_8O	Isobutyraldehyde	69.5	Nonazeotrope		96
1171	$C_4H_8O_2$	Butyric acid	163.3	Nonazeotrope		334

		B-Component		Azeotropic Data		
No.	Formula	Name	B.P.,°C.	B.P.,°C.	Wt.%A	Ref.
A =	C_4H_8O	Butyraldehyde (continued)	74.8			
1172	$C_4H_{10}O$	Isobutyl alcohol	107.9	Nonazeotrope		334
1173	$C_4H_{10}O_2$	1,1-Dimethoxyethane	64.5	Nonazeotrope		334
1174	$C_6H_{10}O$	Mesityl oxide	128.3	Nonazeotrope		334
1175	C_6H_{14}	Hexane	68.7	60	26	334
1176	$C_6H_{14}O_2$	1,1-Dimethoxybutane	114	Nonazeotrope		334
A =	$C_4H_8O_2$	Butyric Acid	162.45			
1177	C_5H_5N	Pyridine	115.5	163.2	92	370
1178	$C_6H_{13}NO$	N,N-Dimethylbutyr- amide, 100 mm.	124.5	130	32.6	295
1179	$C_{11}H_{24}$	Undecane	194.5	162.4	84.5	370
A =	$C_4H_8O_2$	p-Dioxane	101.3			
1180	$C_4H_{10}O$	Butyl alcohol	117.75	Nonazeotrope	v-l	215
1181	$C_4H_{10}O$	Isobutyl alcohol	108	101.3	...	208
1182	C_6H_6	Benzene, 200-760 mm.	...	Nonazeotrope	v-l	124
1183	$C_6H_{14}O$	Isopropyl ether	68.3	Nonazeotrope		334
1184	C_7H_8	Toluene, 200-760 mm.	...	Nonazeotrope	v-l	124
A =	$C_4H_8O_2$	Ethyl Acetate	77.05			
1185	$C_4H_{10}O$	Isobutyl alcohol, 100-760 mm.	...	...	... v-l	316
1186	$C_4H_{10}O_2$	2-Ethoxyethanol	135.1	Nonazeotrope	v-l	220
1187	$C_5H_4O_2$	2-Furaldehyde	161.45	Nonazeotrope		350
1188	C_6H_6	Benzene	80.1	Nonazeotrope	v-l	43, 44
1189	C_6H_{12}	Cyclohexane	80.75	71.6	56 v-l	43, 44
		" 233 mm.	...	38.7	50.1	316
		" 301 mm.	...	45.1	51	316
		" 415 mm.	...	53.6	52.3	316
		" 581 mm.	...	63.0	54.1	316
		" 756 mm.	...	71.1	55.3	316
1190	$C_6H_{12}O_2$	Butyl acetate	126.1	Nonazeotrope		334
1191	$C_6H_{14}O_2$	2-Butoxyethanol	171.1	Nonazeotrope		334
A =	$C_4H_8O_2$	Isobutyric Acid	154.7			
1192	$C_5H_8O_3$	Methyl acetoacetate	171.7	Nonazeotrope		334
1193	C_8H_{10}	Ethylbenzene	136.15	133.0	8.8	84
		" 30 mm.	...	48.0	0.8	84
1194	C_8H_{10}	Mixed xylenes	...	133.0	10.0	84
		" 56 mm.	...	62	1.0	84
A =	$C_4H_8O_2$	Propyl Formate	80.9			
1195	C_6H_{14}	Hexane	68.95	63.6	29.5	324
A =	C_4H_8S	Tetrahydrothiophene	120.79			
1196	$C_6H_{14}S$	Isopropyl sulfide	119.25	118.40	...	70
1197	C_7H_8	Toluene	110.85	Nonazeotrope		70
1198	C_8H_{16}	trans-1,3-Dimethyl- cyclohexane	120.30	115.90	43.1	70
1199	C_8H_{16}	Ethylcyclohexane	131.85	120.46	80.7	70
1200	C_8H_{18}	2,5-Dimethylhexane	109.15	107.95	16.8	70
1201	C_8H_{18}	2-Methylheptane	117.70	113.96	38.2	70
1202	C_8H_{18}	Octane	125.70	117.79	60.3	70
A =	C_4H_9Cl	1-Chlorobutane	77.9			
1203	$C_4H_{10}O$	Butyl alcohol	117.75	Nonazeotrope	v-l	335
A =	$C_4H_9Cl_3Sn$	Butyltin Trichloride	113/17			
1204	$C_8H_{18}Cl_2Sn$	Dibutyltin dichloride, 17 mm.	157	Nonazeotrope		334
1205	$C_{12}H_{27}ClSn$	Tributyltin chloride, 17 mm.	166	Nonazeotrope		334

TABLE I   BINARY SYSTEMS   **41**

		B-Component		Azeotropic Data		
No.	Formula	Name	B.P.,°C.	B.P.,°C.	Wt.%A	Ref.
A =	C₄H₉NO	**Morpholine**	**128.3**			
1206	C₈H₁₈O	Butyl ether	142.1	126.7	73	334
1207	C₉H₁₈O	2,6-Dimethyl-4-heptanone	169.4	128	98	334
A =	C₄H₉NO₃	**2-Methyl-2-nitro-1-Propanol**	...			
1208	C₆H₁₁NO₃	2-Methyl-2-nitro-propyl vinyl ether, 10 mm.	...	71-81	8.6	341
A =	C₄H₁₀O	**Butyl Alcohol**	**117.75**			
1209	C₄H₁₀O	sec-Butyl alcohol	99.5	Nonazeotrope		334
1210	C₄H₁₀O	Isobutyl alcohol, to crit. region	107	Nonazeotrope	v-1	75, 334
		" 750 mm.	...	Nonazeotrope	v-1	335
1211	C₄H₁₀O	Ethyl ether, to crit. region	34.5	Nonazeotrope	v-1	75
1212	C₄H₁₀S	1-Butanethiol, 770 mm.	98	97.8	14.84	181
1213	C₄H₁₁N	Butylamine	77.1	Nonazeotrope		334
1214	C₅H₅N	Pyridine	115.5	118.6	69	v-1 141
1215	C₅H₈O₂	Methyl methacrylate	99.8	Nonazeotrope		147
1216	C₆H₆	Benzene, 45°	...	Nonazeotrope	v-1	24
		"	80.1	Nonazeotrope	v-1	344, 362
1217	C₆H₁₂	Cyclohexane	80.8	79.8	9.5	147, 335
1218	C₆H₁₂O	Butyl vinyl ether	94.2	93.3	7.8	335
1219	C₆H₁₂O	Hexaldehyde	128.3	116.8	77.1	335
1220	C₆H₁₂O₂	Butyl acetate, 50 mm.	...	...	27.3	117
		"	126.2	117.6	67.2	117, 335
1221	C₆H₁₄	Hexane	68.95	68.2	3.2	174, 335
1222	C₆H₁₄O₂	2-Butoxyethanol	171.1	Nonazeotrope	v-1	335
1223	C₇H₈	Toluene	110.7	105.5	27.5	v-1 377
		" 200 mm.	...	66.8	17.7	v-1 124
		" 400 mm.	...	85.45	22.9	v-1 124
		" 600 mm.	...	97.7	26.5	v-1 124
		" 760 mm.	...	105.3	29.7	v-1 124
1224	C₇H₁₂O₂	Butyl acrylate, 100 mm.	69.77	69	75	334
		" 20 mm.	...	39	87.7	76
		" 150 mm.	...	77	92.2	76
		"	147	117	98.2	76
1225	C₇H₁₆	Heptane	98.4	93.85	18	174, 175
		"	98.4	~94	~16	v-1 141
1226	C₇H₁₈SiO	(Trimethylsiloxy) butane	...	Azeotropic		193
1227	C₈H₁₀	Ethylbenzene, 50 mm.	...	...	36.3	v-1 92
		" 100 mm.	...	63.65	42.1	v-1 92
		" 300 mm.	...	...	51.0	v-1 92
		" 500 mm.	...	...	59.7	v-1 92
		" 760 mm.	136.15	115.85	65.1	v-1 92
1228	C₈H₁₈	Octane	125.75	108.45	43.2	174, 175
1229	C₈H₁₈O	Butyl ether	142.1	117.6	82.5	335
1230	C₈H₁₉N	Dibutylamine	159.6	Nonazeotrope		334
1231	C₉H₂₀	Nonane	150.7	115.9	71.5	174, 175
A =	C₄H₁₀O	sec-Butyl Alcohol	**99.5**			
1232	C₆H₁₂O₂	Butyl acetate	126.1	Nonazeotrope		334
1233	C₆H₁₂O₂	sec-Butyl acetate	112.2	Nonazeotrope		334
1234	C₇H₁₄	Methylcyclohexane	101.5	89.7	38.2	v-1 352
1235	C₇H₁₆	Heptane	98.4	88.1	36.7	v-1 352
1236	C₈H₁₄	Diisobutylene	102.3	91	35	37
1237	C₈H₁₈	Iso-octane	99.3	88.0	33.8	v-1 352

		B-Component		Azeotropic Data		
No.	Formula	Name	B.P.,°C.	B.P.,°C.	Wt.%A	Ref.
A =	C$_4$H$_{10}$O	**Isobutyl Alcohol**	**107**			
1238	C$_6$H$_6$	Benzene	80.1	78.36	12	111
		" 111 mm.	...	28.4	2.7	316
		" 240 mm.	...	45.0	4.2	316
		" 525 mm.	...	67.4	6.4	316
		" 760 mm.	80.1	79.3	7.4	316
		" 206 mm.	...	43.0	4.2	256
		" 394 mm.	...	59.5	6.0	256
		" 759 mm.	80.1	79.4	7.9	256
		" 5420 mm.	...	159.9	21.0	256
		" 12,930 mm.	...	207.5	33	256
A =	C$_4$H$_{10}$O	**Ethyl Ether**	**34.5**			
1239	C$_8$H$_{18}$O	Butyl ether, 600 mm.	142.4	Ideal system	v-l	257
A =	C$_4$H$_{10}$O$_2$	**1,2-Dimethoxyethane**	**85.2**			
1240	C$_6$H$_{14}$O	Isopropyl ether	68.3	Nonazeotrope		334
A =	C$_4$H$_{10}$O$_2$	**1,4-Butanediol**	**230**			
1241	C$_6$H$_{12}$O$_2$	4-Vinyloxybutanol	...	Min. b.p.	...	94
A =	C$_4$H$_{10}$O$_2$	**2-Ethoxyethanol**	**134.0**			
1242	C$_5$H$_8$O$_2$	Methyl methacrylate	99.8	Nonazeotrope		147
1243	C$_5$H$_{10}$O$_2$	Propyl acetate	101.6	Nonazeotrope	v-l	220
1244	C$_6$H$_{12}$O$_2$	Butyl acetate	126.2	125.7	13	v-l	221
1245	C$_6$H$_{14}$N$_2$	2,5-Dimethylpiperazine	164	Nonazeotrope		334
1246	C$_6$H$_{14}$O$_3$	2-(2-Ethoxyethoxy) ethanol	202.8	Nonazeotrope		334
1247	C$_8$H$_8$	Styrene, 50 mm.	...	59.8	42.5	v-l	110
1248	C$_8$H$_{10}$	Ethylbenzene, 50 mm.	...	53.9	27.6	v-l	110
		" 57 mm.	60.62	50.0	42 vol. %	291
		" 735 mm.	134.9	126.2	43.3	v-l	167
		"	136.15	128	45	v-l	227
1249	C$_8$H$_{10}$	m-Xylene, 735 mm.	137.9	127.7	48.9	v-l	167
1250	C$_8$H$_{10}$	o-Xylene, 735 mm.	143.1	129.6	57.2	v-l	167
1251	C$_8$H$_{10}$	p-Xylene, 735 mm.	137.4	127.3	47.9	v-l	167
1252	C$_8$H$_{16}$	trans-1,2-Dimethyl-cyclohexane	123.42	115.6	27 vol. %	291
1253	C$_8$H$_{16}$	Ethylcyclohexane	131.78	120.2	33 vol. %	291
1254	C$_8$H$_{16}$	cis-2-Octene	125.6	117.9	28 vol. %	291
1255	C$_8$H$_{18}$	2,5-Dimethylhexane	109.10	105.1	16 vol. %	291
1256	C$_8$H$_{18}$	3,3-Dimethylhexane	111.97	107.1	17 vol. %	291
1257	C$_8$H$_{18}$	3-Ethyl-3-methyl-pentane	118.26	111.7	23 vol. %	291
1258	C$_8$H$_{18}$	Octane	125.75	122.5	33.6	v-l	227
1259	C$_9$H$_{12}$	o-Ethyltoluene	165.15	135.0	91 vol. %	291
1260	C$_9$H$_{12}$	Mesitylene, 735 mm.	163.4	133.7	85.7	v-l	167
1261	C$_9$H$_{18}$	Butylcyclopentane	156.56	130.2	61 vol. %	291
1262	C$_9$H$_{18}$	Isobutylcyclopentane	147.6	127.4	49 vol. %	291
1263	C$_9$H$_{18}$	Isopropylcyclohexane	154.5	129.6	56 vol. %	291
1264	C$_9$H$_{18}$	1-Nonene	146.87	128.1	48 vol. %	291
1265	C$_9$H$_{18}$	Propylcyclohexane	156.72	130.2	59 vol. %	291
1266	C$_9$H$_{20}$	3,3-Diethylpentane	146.17	126.4	45 vol. %	291
1267	C$_9$H$_{20}$	n-Nonane	150.8	128.0	50 vol. %	291
1268	C$_9$H$_{20}$	2,2,3,3-Tetramethyl-pentane	140.27	124.1	40 vol. %	291
1269	C$_9$H$_{20}$	2,2,4,4-Tetramethyl-pentane	122.28	114.3	26 vol. %	291
1270	C$_9$H$_{20}$	2,3,3,4-Tetramethyl-pentane	141.55	124.6	41 vol. %	291
1271	C$_9$H$_{20}$	2,2,3-Trimethylhexane	133.60	120.8	34 vol. %	291
1272	C$_9$H$_{20}$	2,2,4-Trimethylhexane	126.54	116.8	26 vol. %	291
1273	C$_9$H$_{20}$	2,3,3-Trimethylhexane	137.68	122.8	41 vol. %	291
1274	C$_9$H$_{20}$	2,3,5-Trimethylhexane	131.34	119.5	32 vol. %	291
1275	C$_9$H$_{20}$	2,4,4-Trimethylhexane	130.65	119.1	34 vol. %	291
1276	C$_9$H$_{20}$	3,3,4-Trimethylhexane	140.46	124.0	40 vol. %	291

TABLE I   BINARY SYSTEMS   **43**

		B-Component			Azeotropic Data		
No.	Formula	Name	B.P.,°C.	B.P.,°C.	Wt.%A		Ref.
A =	$C_4H_{10}O_2$	2-Ethoxyethanol (continued)	**134.0**				
1277	$C_{10}H_{20}$	tert-Butylcyclohexane	171.5	133.3	73 vol. %		291
A =	$C_4H_{10}O_3$	Diethylene Glycol	**245.5**				
1278	$C_5H_{12}O_3$	2-(2-Methoxyethoxy) ethanol	193.6	Nonazeotrope			334
1279	C_6H_6	Benzene	80.1	Nonazeotrope			334
1280	$C_6H_{12}O_3$	2-(2-Vinyloxyethoxy) ethanol	...	Min. b.p.			94
1281	$C_6H_{14}O_3$	2-(2-Ethoxyethoxy) ethanol	202.8	Nonazeotrope			334
1282	$C_6H_{14}O_4$	Triethylene glycol, 3 mm.	...	Nonazeotrope		v-l	60
1283	C_8H_7N	Indole	253	Azeo. distillation			120
1284	C_8H_{10}	Ethylbenzene	136.15	Azeo. distillation			120
1285	C_8H_{10}	p-Xylene	138.2	Azeo. distillation			120
1286	$C_8H_{18}O_3$	2-(2-Butoxyethoxy) ethanol, 10 mm.	109	Nonazeotrope			334
1287	$C_8H_{18}O_4$	2-[2-(2-Ethoxyethoxy) ethoxy]ethanol, 2 mm.	98	87	43		335
		" 3 mm.	...	135	83.4		60
1288	$C_{10}H_8$	Naphthalene	218.1	Azeo. distillation			120
1289	$C_{11}H_{14}OS$	2-(Benzylmercapto) ethyl vinyl ether	...	Min. b.p.			329
1290	$C_{12}H_9N$	Carbazole, >10 mm.	294	Nonazeotrope			100
1291	$C_{12}H_{10}$	Biphenyl	355.9	Azeo. distillation			120
1292	$C_{12}H_{10}O$	Phenyl ether, 4 mm.	100	...	23		335
1293	$C_{12}H_{24}OS$	2-(2-Ethylhexylthio) ethyl vinyl ether	...	Min. b.p.			329
1294	$C_{12}H_{26}O$	Hexyl ether, 50 mm.	137	129.9	15.5		335
1295	$C_{13}H_{10}$	Fluorene, 10-760 mm.	294	Min. b.p.	...		100
1296	$C_{14}H_{10}$	Phenanthrene, 20 mm.	...	146	93		100
		" 100 mm.	...	180	96.2		100
		" 200 mm.	...	203	98.5		100
		" 300 mm.	...	217	99.5		100
		" 400 mm.	...	226	99.9		100
1297	$C_{14}H_{14}O$	Benzyl ether, 5 mm.	...	...	40		335
1298	$C_{16}H_{34}O$	Bis(2-ethylhexyl)ether, 10 mm.	135	114	...		335
A =	$C_4H_{10}S$	2-Butanethiol	**85.15**				
1299	$C_4H_{10}S$	Isopropyl methyl sulfide	84.76	Nonazeotrope			70
A =	$C_4H_{10}S$	Ethyl Sulfide	**92.07**				
1300	C_6H_6	Benzene	80.10	Nonazeotrope			70
1301	C_6H_{12}	Cyclohexane	80.85	Nonazeotrope			70
1302	C_7H_{14}	trans-1,3-Dimethyl-cyclopentane	90.80	88.89	41.0		70
1303	C_7H_{14}	1,1-Dimethylcyclo-pentane	87.90	86.98	26.1		70
1304	C_7H_{14}	Methylcyclohexane	101.05	92.10	94.5		70
1305	C_7H_{16}	3-Methylhexane	91.60	89.19	48.3		70
1306	C_7H_{16}	2,3-Dimethylpentane	89.90	87.93	38.6		70
1307	C_7H_{16}	2,4-Dimethylpentane	80.55	80.53	2.26		70
1308	C_8H_{18}	2,2,4-Trimethylpentane	99.30	91.44	77.0		70
A =	$C_4H_{10}S$	Isopropyl Methyl Sulfide	**84.76**				
1309	C_6H_{12}	Cyclohexane	80.85	79.76	30		70
1310	C_6H_{12}	Methylcyclopentane	71.85	Nonazeotrope			70
1311	C_7H_{14}	trans-1,3-Dimethyl-cyclopentane	90.80	84.38	80.4		70
1312	C_7H_{14}	1,1-Dimethylcyclo-pentane	87.90	83.62	64.9		70
1313	C_7H_{16}	3-Methylhexane	91.60	84.38	82.4		70

		B-Component		Azeotropic Data		
No.	Formula	Name	B.P.,°C.	B.P.,°C.	Wt.%A	Ref.
A =	$C_4H_{10}S$	Isopropyl Methyl Sulfide (continued)	84.76			
1314	C_7H_{16}	2,3-Dimethylpentane	89.90	83.83	72.8	70
1315	C_7H_{16}	2,4-Dimethylpentane	80.55	79.39	29.7	70
1316	C_7H_{16}	2,2-Dimethylpentane	79.20	78.40	23.3	70
A =	$C_4H_{10}S$	Methyl Propyl Sulfide	95.47			
1317	C_7H_{14}	Ethylcyclopentane	103.45	95.41	90.7	70
1318	C_7H_{14}	Methylcyclohexane	101.05	95.06	78.0	70
1319	C_7H_{14}	trans-1,3-Dimethyl-cyclopentane	90.80	90.11	24.3	70
1320	C_7H_{14}	1,1-Dimethylcyclo-pentane	87.90	87.66	9.7	70
1321	C_7H_{16}	3-Methylhexane	91.60	90.53	32.95	70
1322	C_7H_{16}	2,3-Dimethylpentane	89.90	89.10	22.75	70
1323	C_8H_{18}	2,2-Dimethylhexane	106.85	95.42	94.4	70
1324	C_8H_{18}	2,2,4-Trimethylpentane	99.30	94.00	62.2	70
A =	$C_4H_{10}S_2$	Ethyl Disulfide	154.11			
1325	C_9H_{20}	Nonane	150.65	148.62	41.2	70
1326	$C_{10}H_{22}$	3-Ethyl-3-methyl-heptane	163.00	153.02	80.2	70
A =	$C_4H_{11}N$	Diethylamine	55.5			
1327	$C_6H_{14}O$	Isopropyl ether	68.3	Nonazeotrope		334
1328	$C_6H_{15}NO$	2-(Diethylamino) ethanol	162.1	Nonazeotrope		334
A =	$C_4H_{11}NO_2$	2,2'-Iminodiethanol	126/2 mm.			
1329	$C_6H_{15}NO_3$	2,2',2''-Nitrilotri-ethanol, 2 mm.	195	Nonazeotrope		334
A =	$C_5Cl_2F_6$	1,2-Dichlorohexa-fluorocyclopentene	90.6			
1330	$C_8F_{16}O$	Perfluorocyclic oxide	102.6	90.4	80	v-1 354
A =	C_5F_{10}	Perfluorocyclopentane	...			
1331	C_5F_{12}	Perfluoropentane, 9.6°-25° C.	...	Nonazeotrope		v-1 237
1332	C_6F_{14}	Perfluorohexane, 15°-25° C.	...	Nonazeotrope		v-1 237
A =	$C_5H_4F_8O$	2,2,3,3,4,4,5,5-Octafluoro-1-pentanol	...			
1333	$C_5H_{12}O$	Active amyl alcohol	128.5	Nonazeotrope		330
1334	$C_5H_{12}O$	Isoamyl alcohol	132.0	Nonazeotrope		330
A =	$C_5H_4O_2$	2-Furaldehyde	161.45			
1335	$C_5H_6O_2$	Furfuryl alcohol, 25 mm.	...	Nonazeotrope		v-1 348
1336	C_6H_6	Benzene	80.1	Nonazeotrope		v-1 52, 331
1337	C_6H_{12}	Cyclohexane	80.75	Nonazeotrope		v-1 52, 331
1338	C_7H_{14}	Methylcyclohexane	101.05	100.8	4.1	v-1 114
1339	C_7H_{16}	Heptane	98.40	98.3	5.3	v-1 114
A =	C_5H_5N	Pyridine	115.5			
1340	$C_5H_{11}N$	Piperidine	106	105.8	3.4	147
1341	$C_5H_{12}O$	3-Pentanol	115.6	117.4	45	334
1342	C_7H_8	Toluene	110.8	110.1	22.2	v-1 141, 371
1343	C_7H_{16}	Heptane	98.40	95.60	25.3	355, 373
		"	98.40	95	13.3	v-1 141
1344	C_8H_{10}	Ethylbenzene	136.15	Nonazeotrope		363
1345	C_8H_{10}	o-Xylene	143.6	Nonazeotrope		372

TABLE I   BINARY SYSTEMS   **45**

		B-Component		Azeotropic Data		
No.	Formula	Name	B.P.,°C.	B.P.,°C.	Wt.%A	Ref.
A =	C_5H_5N	**Pyridine (continued)**	**115.5**			
1346	C_8H_{18}	Octane	125.75	109.5	56.1	355
1347	C_9H_{20}	Nonane	150.7	115.1	89.9	355
1348	$C_{10}H_8N_2$	2,2'-Dipyridyl	274	Nonazeotrope		147
1349	$C_{10}H_{22}$	Decane	173.3	Nonazeotrope		355
A =	C_5H_6S	**2-Methylthiophene**	**111.92**			
1350	C_7H_{16}	Heptane	98.40	97.77	2.2	70
1351	C_8H_{18}	2-Methylheptane	117.70	109.97	67.8	70
1352	C_8H_{18}	2,5-Dimethylhexane	109.15	106.12	39.6	70
1353	C_8H_{18}	2,2-Dimethylhexane	106.85	104.62	33.2	70
A =	C_5H_6S	**3-Methylthiophene**	**114.96**			
1354	C_7H_{14}	Ethylcyclopentane	103.45	102.82	3.9	70
1355	C_7H_{16}	Heptane	98.40	Nonazeotrope		70
1356	C_8H_{16}	trans-1,3-Dimethyl-cyclohexane	120.3	113.17	66	70
1357	C_8H_{16}	1,1,2-Trimethylcyclo-pentane	113.75	110.47	43.2	70
1358	C_8H_{18}	Octane	125.70	114.15	82	70
1359	C_8H_{18}	2-Methylheptane	117.70	111.86	58.8	70
1360	C_8H_{18}	2,5-Dimethylhexane	109.15	107.12	31.7	70
A =	C_5H_8	**Isoprene**	**34.3**			
1361	C_5H_{10}	3-Methyl-1-butene	21.2	Nonazeotrope		248
1362	C_5H_{10}	2-Methyl-1-butene	32	Nonazeotrope		248
1363	C_5H_{10}	2-Methyl-2-butene	37.7	Nonazeotrope		248
1364	C_5H_{12}	2-Methylbutane	27.6	Nonazeotrope		248
1365	C_5H_{12}	Pentane, 758 mm.	36	33.6	72.5	v-l 248
A =	$C_5H_8Cl_4$	**Tetrachloropentane**	...			
1366	$C_7H_{12}Cl_4$	Tetrachloroheptane, 12-150 mm.	...	Nonazeotrope		v-l 250
A =	C_5H_8O	**Cyclopentanone**	**129.5**			
1367	$C_5H_{12}O$	Active amyl alcohol	128.5	Nonazeotrope		330
1368	$C_5H_{12}O$	Isoamyl alcohol	131.85	127.8	60	v-l 87, 88
		"	131.85	129.4	...	314
		"	131.85	Nonazeotrope		2
1369	$C_5H_{12}O$	2-Methyl-1-butanol	128.9	127	...	87, 88
		"	128.9	124.6	...	314
A =	$C_5H_8O_2$	**Ethyl Acrylate**	**99.3**			
1370	$C_6H_{14}O$	Isopropyl ether	68.3	Nonazeotrope		334
A =	$C_5H_8O_2$	**Methyl Methacrylate**	**61.8/200 mm.**			
1371	$C_8H_{14}O_2$	Butyl methacrylate, 200 mm.	117.7	Nonazeotrope		147
1372	$C_8H_{14}O_3$	2-Ethoxyethyl methacrylate, 200 mm.	134.3	Nonazeotrope		147
A =	$C_5H_8O_2$	**2,4-Pentanedione**	**140.2**			
1373	$C_5H_8O_2$	Isopropenyl acetate	96.5	Nonazeotrope		147
A =	C_5H_{10}	**Cyclopentane**	**49.4**			
1374	C_6H_6	Benzene	80.1	Nonazeotrope		v-l 230
1375	C_6H_{14}	2,2-Dimethylbutane	49.7	49.1	82.3	214
A =	C_5H_{10}	**3-Methyl-1-butene**	**22.5**			
1376	C_5H_{12}	2-Methylbutane	27.6	Nonazeotrope		248
A =	C_5H_{10}	**2-Methyl-2-butene**	**37.7**			
1377	C_5H_{12}	Pentane	36.15	Nonazeotrope		248

		B-Component		Azeotropic Data		
No.	Formula	Name	B.P.,°C.	B.P.,°C.	Wt.%A	Ref.
A =	$C_5H_{10}O$	3-Methyl-2-butanone	95.4			
1378	C_6H_{12}	Cyclohexane	80.75	...	14.8	256
1379	C_7H_{16}	Heptane	98.4	...	48	256
A =	$C_5H_{10}O$	2-Pentanone	102.35			
1380	C_6H_{12}	Cyclohexane	80.75	...	5.0	256
A =	$C_5H_{10}O$	3-Pentanone	102			
1381	C_7H_{14}	Methylcyclohexane	101.15	...	40	256
1382	C_7H_{16}	Heptane	98.4	...	35	256
1383	C_8H_{16}	1,3-Dimethylcyclo-hexane	120.7	...	83	256
1384	C_8H_{18}	2,5-Dimethylhexane	109.4	...	60	256
A =	$C_5H_{10}O_2$	Isopropyl Acetate	88.7			
1385	C_6H_8O	2,5-Dimethylfuran	93.3	Nonazeotrope		334
A =	$C_5H_{10}O_2$	Valeric Acid	186.35			
1386	$C_7H_{15}NO$	N,N-Dimethylvaler-amide, 100 mm.	141	145.8	30.8	295
A =	C_5H_{12}	Pentane	36.15			
1387	C_6H_6	Benzene	80.2	Nonazeotrope	v-1	52, 229
1388	C_6H_{12}	Cyclohexane	80.75	Nonazeotrope	v-1	231
1389	C_6H_{12}	Methylcyclopentane	72.0	Nonazeotrope	v-1	52, 231
1390	C_7F_{16}	Perfluoroheptane, crit. region	82.5	Azeotrope	v-1	155
1391	C_7H_{14}	Methylcyclohexane	101.15	Nonazeotrope	v-1	52, 231
A =	$C_5H_{12}O$	Amyl Alcohol	137.8			
1392	C_6H_6	Benzene	80.2	Nonazeotrope	v-1	344
1393	$C_6H_{10}O$	Methylcyclopentanone	138	Min. b.p.	87, 88,	314
1394	$C_6H_{14}N_2$	2,5-Dimethylpiperazine	164	Nonazeotrope		334
1395	C_8H_{18}	C_8 paraffins	120-130	Min. b.p.		314
1396	C_8H_{18}	Octane	125.75	121.8	...	314
1397	$C_{11}H_{24}O_2$	Diamyloxymethane	...	Nonazeotrope		334
A =	$C_5H_{12}O$	Active Amyl Alcohol	128.5			
1398	$C_5H_{12}O$	Isoamyl alcohol	131	Nonazeotrope	v-1	246
1399	C_6H_5Cl	Chlorobenzene	132	124.4	43	330
1400	C_6H_5FO	o-Fluorophenol	...	Nonazeotrope		330
1401	C_6H_7N	2-Picoline	129	132.8	49	330
1402	$C_6H_{10}O$	Mesityl oxide	129.5	Nonazeotrope		330
1403	C_7H_7F	o-Fluorotoluene	114	112.0	16	330
1404	C_7H_8	Toluene	111	109.9	12	330
1405	C_7H_9N	2,6-Lutidine	144	Nonazeotrope		330
1406	$C_7H_{14}O$	2,4-Dimethyl-3-pentanone	125	124.1	21	330
1407	$C_7H_{15}N$	1,2-Dimethylpiperidine	128	130.3	...	330
1408	$C_7H_{15}N$	2,6-Dimethylpiperidine	128	130.7	54	330
1409	C_8H_{10}	Ethylbenzene	136	125.0	53	330
1410	C_8H_{18}	n-Octane	126.0	117.0	34	330
1411	C_9H_{20}	2,2,5-Trimethylhexane	124	115.5	29	330
A =	$C_5H_{12}O$	Isoamyl Alcohol	131			
1412	$C_5H_{12}S$	3-Methyl-1-butanethiol	116	115.6	22.89	181
1413	C_6H_5Cl	Chlorobenzene	132	123.9	38	330
1414	C_6H_5FO	o-Fluorophenol	...	Nonazeotrope		330
1415	C_6H_7N	2-Picoline	129	132.8	61	330
1416	$C_6H_{10}O$	Mesityl oxide	129.5	Nonazeotrope		330
1417	C_7H_n	C_7 hydrocarbons	95-120	Min. b.p.		314
1418	C_7H_7F	o-Fluorotoluene	114	112.1	14	330
1419	C_7H_8	Toluene	111	109.7	10	330, 371

TABLE I   BINARY SYSTEMS 47

		B-Component			Azeotropic Data		
No.	Formula	Name	B.P.,°C.	B.P.,°C.	Wt.%A		Ref.
A =	$C_5H_{12}O$	**Isoamyl Alcohol** (continued)	**131**				
1420	C_7H_9N	2,6-Lutidine, 70 mm.	...	Max. b.p.			330
		"	144	Nonazeotrope			330
1421	$C_7H_{14}O$	2,4-Dimethyl-3-pentanone	125	124.5	8		330
1422	$C_7H_{15}N$	1,2-Dimethyl-piperidine	128	132.5	81		330
1423	$C_7H_{15}N$	2,6-Dimethyl-piperidine	128	132.6	76		330
1424	C_8H_{10}	Ethylbenzene	136	125.7	49		330
1425	C_8H_{18}	n-Octane	126	117.0	30		330
1426	C_9H_{20}	$\overline{2}$,2,5-Trimethylhexane	124	116.0	26		330
A =	$C_5H_{12}O$	**2-Methyl-1-Butanol**	**128.9**				
1427	C_7H_n	C_7 hydrocarbons	95-120	Min. b.p.			314
1428	C_7H_8	Toluene	110.7	Min. b.p.			314
A =	$C_5H_{12}O$	**2-Methyl-2-butanol**	**101.7**				
1429	C_6H_6	Benzene	80.2	80.0	15		52
		" 715 mm.	...	...	4.95	v-l	272
1430	C_7H_8	Toluene	110.7	100.5	56		52
		" 715 mm.	...	...	32.5	v-l	272
A =	$C_5H_{12}O_3$	**2-(2-Methoxyethoxy) ethanol**	**192.95**				
1431	$C_8H_6Cl_2$	$\underline{ar}$-Dichlorostyrene, 15 mm.	...	86-90	...		49
		" 29 mm.	...	100-101	...		49
1432	C_9H_{12}	p-Ethyltoluene	161.99	161.4	9 vol. %		291
1433	C_9H_{12}	m-Ethyltoluene	161.31	160.9	13 vol. %		291
1434	C_9H_{12}	o-Ethyltoluene	165.15	164.3	16 vol. %		291
1435	C_9H_{12}	$\overline{1}$,2,3-Trimethyl-benzene	176.08	173.4	26 vol. %		291
1436	C_9H_{12}	1,2,4-Trimethyl-benzene	169.35	167.9	21 vol. %		291
1437	C_9H_{12}	Mesitylene	164.72	163.8	12 vol. %		291
1438	$C_{10}H_{14}$	Butylbenzene	183.27	177.9	32 vol. %		291
1439	$C_{10}H_{14}$	sec-Butylbenzene	173.30	170.7	16 vol. %		291
1440	$C_{10}H_{14}$	$\underline{tert}$-Butylbenzene	169.11	167.6	13 vol. %		291
1441	$C_{10}H_{14}$	Isobutylbenzene	172.76	170.3	24 vol. %		291
1442	$C_{10}H_{14}$	m-Diethylbenzene	181.13	176.3	29 vol. %		291
1443	$C_{10}H_{14}$	$\overline{p}$-Diethylbenzene	183.78	177.9	31 vol. %		291
1444	$C_{10}H_{14}$	5-Ethyl-$\underline{m}$-xylene	183.75	177.9	30 vol. %		291
1445	$C_{10}H_{14}$	p-Cymene	177.10	173.3	22 vol. %		291
1446	$C_{10}H_{14}$	$\overline{1}$,2,3,5-Tetramethyl-benzene	197.93	185.9	48 vol. %		291
1447	$C_{11}H_{10}$	2-Methylnaphthalene	241.1	Nonazeotrope			98
1448	$C_{11}H_{16}$	$\underline{tert}$-Amylbenzene	198.1	182.8	40 vol. %		291
1449	$C_{11}H_{22}$	$\underline{tert}$-Amylcyclohexane	198.1	180.6	40 vol. %		291
1450	$C_{11}H_{24}$	$\overline{n}$-Undecane	195.88	178.7	40 vol. %		291
1451	$C_{12}H_{26}$	$\overline{n}$-Dodecane, 217 mm.	169.79	144.2	52 vol. %		291
1452	$C_{12}H_{26}$	$\overline{2}$,2,4,4,6-Pentamethyl-heptane	185.6	173.6	30 vol. %		291
1453	$C_{12}H_{26}$	2,2,4,6,6-Pentamethyl-heptane	177.9	168.9	23 vol. %		291
1454	$C_{13}H_{26}$	1-Tridecene	232.78	191.6	70 vol. %		291
A =	$C_6F_{12}O$	**Perfluorocyclic Ether**	...				
1455	C_6F_{14}	Perfluorohexane, 25°	...	Nonazeotrope		v-l	237
A =	C_6F_{14}	**Perfluorohexane**	...				
1456	C_6H_{14}	Hexane, 325 mm.	...	25	83.4	v-l	79
		" 479 mm.	...	35	83.7	v-l	79
		" 689 mm.	...	45	80.0	v-l	79

		B-Component		Azeotropic Data		
No.	Formula	Name	B.P.,°C.	B.P.,°C.	Wt.%A	Ref.
A =	C_6F_{14}	Perfluorohexane (continued)	...			
1457	$C_{12}F_{27}N$	Tris(perfluorobutyl) amine, 25°	...	Nonazeotrope	v-1	237
A =	$C_6H_3Cl_3$	1,2,4-Trichlorobenzene	...			
1458	$C_9H_6N_2O_2$	2,4-Tolylene diisocyanate, 40 mm.	...	Nonazeotrope	v-1	119
A =	$C_6H_4Cl_2$	o-Dichlorobenzene	67.0/15			
1459	$C_9H_6O_2N_2$	2,4-Tolylene diisocyanate, 15 mm.	128.7	Nonazeotrope		147
1460	$C_{15}H_{10}O_2N_2$	Di-p-isocyanatodiphenylmethane, 5 mm.	192.0	Nonazeotrope		147
A =	C_6H_5Br	Bromobenzene	156.1			
1461	$C_6H_{12}O$	Cyclohexanol,				
		" 250 mm.	127.0	113.6	85.5	v-1 318
		" 500 mm.	144.4	136.8	81.5	v-1 318
		" 730 mm.	158.6	150.6	74.8	v-1 318
A =	C_6H_5Cl	Chlorobenzene	131.8			
1462	C_6H_{14}	n-Hexane	68.95	Nonazeotrope		52
1463	$C_9H_6N_2O_2$	2,4-Tolylene diisocyanate, 40 mm.	...	Nonazeotrope	v-1	119
A =	C_6H_5F	Fluorobenzene	84.9			
1464	C_6H_6	Benzene	80.1	Ideal system	v-1	12
A =	$C_6H_5NO_2$	Nitrobenzene	210.85			
1465	C_6H_{12}	Cyclohexane	80.75	Nonazeotrope		52
A =	C_6H_6	Benzene	80.1			
1466	C_6H_{12}	Cyclohexane	80.75	77.6	51.2	v-1 44, 191, 343
		"	80.75	77.4	52.5	74, 111
		" 128 mm.	...	28.4	47.6	316
		" 155 mm.	...	33.1	48.0	316
		" 287 mm.	...	48.3	49.3	316
		" 307 mm.	...	50.4	49.4	316
		" 495 mm.	...	63.7	50.8	316
		" 602 mm.	...	69.8	51.3	316
		" 760 mm.	...	77.56	51.9	316
		" 14.7 p.s.i.a.	...	77.4	50.2	v-1 321
		" 66.7 p.s.i.a.	...	137.1	61.5	v-1 321
		" 118.0 p.s.i.a.	...	165.8	67.0	v-1 321
		" 186.8 p.s.i.a.	...	193.0	71.5	v-1 321
		" 66.7 p.s.i.a.	...	...	59.7	v-1 276
		" 116.5 p.s.i.a.	...	...	64.9	v-1 276
		" 165.9 p.s.i.a.	...	...	67.6	v-1 276
		" 217.0 p.s.i.a.	...	...	71	v-1 276
		" 268.7 p.s.i.a.	...	...	74	v-1 276
1467	C_6H_{12}	Methylcyclopentane	71.85	71.7	16	v-1 230
1468	$C_6H_{12}O$	4-Methyl-2-pentanone, 450-760 mm.	...	Nonazeotrope	v-1	66
1469	C_6H_{14}	Hexane	68.95	Nonazeotrope	v-1	229
		" 4-18 atm.	...	Nonazeotrope	v-1	276
1470	C_7F_{14}	Perfluoromethylcyclohexane	73-78	59	...	51
1471	C_7F_{16}	Perfluoroheptane	83	61	...	51
1472	C_7H_{14}	Methylcyclohexane	101.05	Nonazeotrope	v-1	230
1473	C_7H_{16}	2,3-Dimethylpentane	89.79	79.4	78.8	v-1 190
1474	C_7H_{16}	2,4-Dimethylpentane	81	>75	48.4	51
1475	C_7H_{16}	Heptane, 180-450 mm.	...	Nonazeotrope	v-1	240
		"	98.4	Nonazeotrope	v-1	229

TABLE I   BINARY SYSTEMS   **49**

		B-Component			Azeotropic Data		
No.	Formula	Name	B.P.,°C.	B.P.,°C.	Wt.%A		Ref.
A =	C_6H_6	Benzene (continued)	80.1				
1476	$C_8F_{18}O$	Perfluorobutyl ether	100	68	...		51
1477	C_8H_{18}	Octane	125.75	Nonazeotrope			52
1478	C_8H_{18}	2,2,4-Trimethyl-pentane, 35°-75° C.	...	Nonazeotrope		v-l	345
1479	$C_8H_{18}O_3$	2-(2-Butoxyethoxy) ethanol	230.6	Nonazeotrope			334
A =	C_6H_6O	Phenol	181.42				
1480	$C_6H_{10}O$	Cyclohexanone, 50 mm.	73	...	71.5		76
		"	155.6	Azeotropic			57
		" 50 mm.	...	Max. b.p.	75.8		334
1481	$C_6H_{10}O_4$	Ethylene diacetate	189.86	195.53	39.2		253
1482	$C_6H_{12}O$	Cyclohexanol, 60 mm.	...	111	70		76
		" 70 mm.	...	111	73		57
		" 90 mm.	...	120	70	v-l	57
		" 200 mm.	...	140	71		76
		"	160.65	180	87		76
1483	$C_8H_8O_2$	Phenyl acetate	195.14	195.89	8.9		253
1484	$C_8H_{18}O$	2-Ethyl-1-hexanol, 25 mm.	...	95.6	95		34, 335
1485	C_9H_{10}	α-Methylstyrene	...	162	7		303
1486	C_9H_{12}	Cumene	152.8	149	2		76
1487	C_9H_{12}	Propylbenzene	158.9	158.5	14		324
1488	$C_9H_{14}SiO$	(Trimethylsiloxy) benzene	181.9	175.5	...		193
A =	$C_6H_6O_2$	Pyrocatechol	245.9				
1489	$C_{12}H_{18}$	1,3,5-Triethylbenzene	215.5	214.7	8.9		324
A =	C_6H_7N	Aniline	184.35				
1490	$C_6H_{12}O$	Cyclohexanol	...	Nonazeotrope		v-l	242
1491	$C_6H_{13}N$	Cyclohexylamine	134	Nonazeotrope			147, 242
1492	C_6H_{14}	Hexane, 556-731 mm.	...	Nonazeotrope		v-l	356
1493	C_7H_8	Toluene	110.7	...	...	v-l	138
1494	C_7H_9N	N-Methylaniline, 95°-145°	...	Nonazeotrope		v-l	59
1495	C_7H_{16}	Heptane	98.4	...	...	v-l	138
1496	$C_8H_{11}N$	N,N-Dimethylaniline, 36.7 mm.	...	95	74.5	v-l	59
		" 101.4 mm.	...	120	76.1	v-l	59
		" 243.1 mm.	...	145	77.5	v-l	59
1497	C_8H_{18}	Iso-octane, 86-741 mm.	...	Nonazeotrope		v-l	356
1498	$C_{10}H_{14}$	p-Cymene, 50 mm.	...	...	21.3	v-l	92
		" 100 mm.	...	106.3	23	v-l	92
		" 300 mm.	...	...	...	v-l	92
		" 500 mm.	...	...	...	v-l	92
		" 760 mm.	...	172.80	31.3	v-l	92
A =	C_6H_7N	2-Picoline	128.8				
1499	$C_6H_{12}O_3$	Paraldehyde	124.5	Nonazeotrope			334
1500	C_8H_{18}	Octane	125.75	121.12	42		369
1501	C_9H_{20}	Nonane	150.7	129.2	84.1		369
A =	C_6H_7N	3-Picoline	144				
1502	C_7H_9N	2,6-Lutidine	144.06	143.5	27.3	v-l	27
A =	C_6H_8ClN	Aniline Hydro-chloride	...				
1503	$C_{12}H_{11}N$	Diphenylamine, 100 mm.	...	...	45.8		153
		" 250 mm.	...	...	48		153
		" 350 mm.	265	215	50		153
		" 740 mm.	...	233	65		153
		" 2500 mm.	...	270	...		153

		B-Component		Azeotropic Data		
No.	Formula	Name	B.P.,°C.	B.P.,°C.	Wt.%A	Ref.
A =	$C_6H_8N_2$	2-Amino-3-methyl-pyridine	221			
1504	$C_{11}H_{10}$	1-Methylnaphthalene,				
		" 20 mm.	...	115	68.2	98, 99
		" 50 mm.	...	136	75.2	98, 99
		" 150 mm.	...	166	89.7	98, 99
		" 290 mm.	...	187	96.4	98, 99
		" 400 mm.	...	198	98.7	98, 99
		" 760 mm.	244.8	Nonazeotrope		98, 99
1505	$C_{11}H_{10}$	2-Methylnaphthalene,				
		" 16 mm.	...	109	57.5	98, 99
		" 50 mm.	...	137	69.5	98, 99
		" 150 mm.	...	165	76.8	98, 99
		" 400 mm.	...	196	92	98, 99
		" 550 mm.	...	209	96	98, 99
		" 760 mm.	241.1	Nonazeotrope		98, 99
A =	$C_6H_{10}O$	Cyclohexanone	155.6			
1506	$C_6H_{12}O$	Cyclohexanol, 100 mm.	...	Nonazeotrope	v-l	57
A =	$C_6H_{10}O$	Mesityl Oxide	128.3			
1507	$C_6H_{12}O$	4-Methyl-2-pentanone	116.2	Nonazeotrope		334
1508	$C_6H_{12}O_2$	4-Hydroxy-4-methyl-2-pentanone	169.2	Nonazeotrope		334
1509	$C_7H_{12}O$	3-Hepten-2-one	162.9	Nonazeotrope		334
1510	$C_8H_{16}O_2$	4-Methyl-2-pentyl acetate	146.1	Nonazeotrope		334
1511	$C_9H_{18}O$	2,6-Dimethyl-4-heptanone	169.4	Nonazeotrope		334
A =	C_6H_{12}	Cyclohexane	80.85			
1512	$C_6H_{12}O$	Cyclohexanol	161.1	Nonazeotrope		334
1513	$C_6H_{12}O$	4-Methyl-2-pentanone, 450-760 mm.	...	Nonazeotrope	v-l	66
1514	$C_6H_{13}N$	Cyclohexylamine	...	Nonazeotrope	v-l	242
1515	C_6H_{14}	Hexane	68.95	Nonazeotrope	v-l	231
1516	C_7H_8	Toluene	110.7	Nonazeotrope	v-l	230
1517	C_7H_{16}	2,4-Dimethylpentane	80.5	80.2	48.6	214
1518	C_7H_{16}	Heptane	98.4	...	...	v-l 52, 231
1519	C_7H_{16}	2,2,3-Trimethylbutane	80.8	80.0	46.6	214
A =	C_6H_{12}	Methylcyclopentane	71.72			
1520	C_6H_{14}	Hexane, 200-760 mm.	68.95	Nonazeotrope	v-l	85, 231
1521	C_7H_8	Toluene	110.7	Nonazeotrope	v-l	230
A =	$C_6H_{12}O$	Cyclohexanol	161			
1522	$C_7H_{12}O_2$	Cyclohexyl formate, 50 mm.	...	79.4	50	147
1523	$C_8H_{14}O$	Cyclohexyl vinyl ether, 45 mm.	...	71-80	21	341
A =	$C_6H_{12}O$	4-Methyl-2-pentanone	116.2			
1524	$C_8H_{16}O_2$	4-Methyl-2-pentyl acetate	146.1	Nonazeotrope		334
1525	$C_9H_{18}O$	2,6-Dimethyl-4-heptanone	169.4	Nonazeotrope		334
A =	$C_6H_{12}O_2$	Butyl Acetate	126.1			
1526	$C_6H_{12}O_2$	sec-Butyl acetate	112.2	Nonazeotrope		334
1527	$C_6H_{14}O_2$	2-Butoxyethanol	171.1	Nonazeotrope		334
1528	$C_8H_{18}O$	Butyl ether	142.1	125.9	95	334

TABLE I   BINARY SYSTEMS   **51**

No.	Formula	Name	B.P.,°C.	B.P.,°C.	Wt.%A	Ref.
		B-Component		Azeotropic Data		

A = $C_6H_{12}O_2$ Hexanoic Acid   205.15

No.	Formula	Name	B.P.,°C.	B.P.,°C.	Wt.%A	Ref.
1529	$C_8H_{16}O_2$	Octanoic acid, 20-100 mm.	...	Nonazeotrope	v-l	289
1530	$C_8H_{17}NO$	N,N-Dimethylhexan-amide, 100 mm.	...	Max. b.p.		

A = $C_6H_{12}O_2$ 4-Hydroxy-4-methyl 2-Pentanone   166

No.	Formula	Name	B.P.,°C.	B.P.,°C.	Wt.%A	Ref.
1531	C_9H_{12}	x-Ethyltoluene, 20 mm.	...	<80	25	353

A = $C_6H_{12}SO_2$ 2,4-Dimethylsulfolane   ...

No.	Formula	Name	B.P.,°C.	B.P.,°C.	Wt.%A	Ref.
1532	$C_{15}H_{18}$	Amyl naphthalene, 20 mm.	...	151	75	225
1533	$C_{16}H_{34}$	Hexadecane, 20 mm.	...	142	75	225

A = $C_6H_{12}O_3$ 2-Ethoxyethyl Acetate   156.2

No.	Formula	Name	B.P.,°C.	B.P.,°C.	Wt.%A	Ref.
1534	C_7H_8	Toluene	110.6	Nonazeotrope		334

A = $C_6H_{12}O_3$ Paraldehyde   124

No.	Formula	Name	B.P.,°C.	B.P.,°C.	Wt.%A	Ref.
1535	C_8H_{10}	m-Xylene	139	Nonazeotrope		113
1536	C_8H_{10}	p-Xylene	138.4	Nonazeotrope		113

A = C_6H_{14} Hexane   68.95

No.	Formula	Name	B.P.,°C.	B.P.,°C.	Wt.%A	Ref.
1537	C_7F_{16}	Perfluoroheptane, crit. region	...	Azeotropic	v-l	155
1538	C_7H_8	Toluene	110.7	Nonazeotrope		52
		" 150-760 mm.	...	Nonazeotrope	v-l	229
1539	C_7H_{14}	Methylcyclohexane	101.15	Nonazeotrope	v-l	52, 231

A = $C_6H_{14}O$ 2-Ethyl-1-butanol   147.0

No.	Formula	Name	B.P.,°C.	B.P.,°C.	Wt.%A	Ref.
1540	$C_8H_{16}O$	2-Ethylhexaldehyde	163.6	Nonazeotrope		334
1541	$C_8H_{17}Cl$	3-(Chloromethyl) heptane, 50 mm.	89	77	61	335
		" 100 mm.	106.9	92	68	335

A = $C_6H_{14}O$ Hexyl Alcohol   157.1

No.	Formula	Name	B.P.,°C.	B.P.,°C.	Wt.%A	Ref.
1542	$C_8H_{16}O_2$	2-Ethylbutyl acetate	162.3	154.4	72.5	335

A = $C_6H_{14}O$ Isopropyl Ether   68.3

No.	Formula	Name	B.P.,°C.	B.P.,°C.	Wt.%A	Ref.
1543	$C_6H_{14}O_2$	1,2-Diethoxyethane	121.1	Nonazeotrope		334

A = $C_6H_{14}O$ 4-Methyl-2-pentanol   131.8

No.	Formula	Name	B.P.,°C.	B.P.,°C.	Wt.%A	Ref.
1544	$C_8H_{16}O_2$	4-Methyl-2-pentyl acetate	146.1	Nonazeotrope		334

A = $C_6H_{14}OS$ 2-Butylthioethanol   ...

No.	Formula	Name	B.P.,°C.	B.P.,°C.	Wt.%A	Ref.
1545	$C_8H_{16}OS$	2-Butylthioethyl vinyl ether	...	Min. b.p.		329

A = $C_6H_{14}O_2$ 2-Butoxyethanol   171.2

No.	Formula	Name	B.P.,°C.	B.P.,°C.	Wt.%A	Ref.
1546	C_9H_{12}	Cumene	152.4	151.7	10.3	168
1547	C_9H_{16}	cis-Hexahydroindan	167.7	159.9	38 vol. %	291
1548	$C_{10}H_{14}$	Butylbenzene	183.4	169.6	73.4	168
1549	$C_{10}H_{14}$	sec-Butylbenzene	173.3	166.0	47.9	168
1550	$C_{10}H_{14}$	tert-Butylbenzene	169.1	164.4	39.1	168
1551	$C_{10}H_{14}$	p-Cymene	177.2	167.4	56.6	168
1552	$C_{10}H_{20}$	n-Butylcyclohexane	180.95	165.6	56 vol. %	291
1553	$C_{10}H_{20}$	sec-Butylcyclohexane	179.3	165.1	53 vol. %	291
1554	$C_{10}H_{20}$	Isobutylcyclohexane	171.3	161.5	40 vol. %	291
1555	$C_{10}H_{20}$	cis-1-Methyl-4-isopropylcyclo-hexane	172.7	162.0	45 vol. %	291
1556	$C_{10}H_{20}$	trans-1-methyl-4-isopropylcyclo-hexane	170.5	160.9	41 vol. %	291

	No.	Formula	Name	B.P.,°C.	B.P.,°C.	Wt.%A	Ref.
			B-Component		Azeotropic Data		

	No.	Formula	Name	B.P.,°C.	B.P.,°C.	Wt.%A	Ref.
A =		$C_6H_{14}O_2$	2-Butoxyethanol (continued)	171.2			
	1557	$C_{10}H_{22}$	3,3,5-Trimethyl-heptane	155.5	151.6	23 vol. %	291
A =		$C_6H_{14}O_2$	Hexylene Glycol	...			
	1558	C_8H_{10}	Ethylbenzene, 400 mm.	...	Nonazeotrope	v-1	271
	1559	C_8H_{16}	Ethylcyclohexane, 400 mm.	...	Nonazeotrope	v-1	271
A =		$C_6H_{14}O_3$	Dipropylene Glycol	...			
	1560	$C_{10}H_8$	Naphthalene	218.1	142.9	12.4 v-1	204
	1561	$C_{11}H_{10}$	2-Methylnaphthalene	241.1	Nonazeotrope		98
A =		$C_6H_{14}O_3$	2-(2-Ethoxyethoxy) ethanol	202.8			
	1562	$C_8H_{18}O_3$	Bis(2-ethoxyethyl) ether	188.4	Nonazeotrope		334
			" 10 mm.	72	Nonazeotrope		334
	1563	$C_{11}H_{10}$	2-Methylnaphthalene	241.1	Nonazeotrope		98
A =		$C_6H_{14}O_3$	Triethylene Glycol	288.7			
	1564	$C_{12}H_9N$	Carbazole	294	Nonazeotrope		100
			" Low press.	...	Min. b.p.		100
	1565	$C_{12}H_{10}O$	Phenyl ether, 4 mm.	102	Nonazeotrope		334
	1566	$C_{13}H_{10}$	Fluorene	294	Nonazeotrope		100
			" High press.	...	Min. b.p.		100
	1567	$C_{14}H_{10}$	Phenanthrene, Low press.	340	Min. b.p.		100
			Glycol decreases with decreasing pressure				
	1568	$C_{14}H_{14}O$	Benzyl ether, 5 mm.	145.5	...	28	335
A =		$C_6H_{15}NO_2$	1,1'-Iminodi-2-propanol	133/10			
	1569	$C_9H_{21}NO_3$	1,1',1"-Nitrilotri-2-propanol, 10 mm.	177	Nonazeotrope		334
A =		C_7F_{16}	Perfluoroheptane	82.5			
	1570	C_7H_{16}	Heptane, crit. region	...	Azeotropic	v-1	155
	1571	$C_8F_{16}O$	Perfluorocyclic oxide	102.6	Nonazeotrope	v-1	354
	1572	C_8H_{18}	Octane, crit. region	...	Azeotropic	v-1	155
	1573	C_9H_{20}	Nonane, crit. region	...	Nonazeotrope	v-1	155
A =		$C_7H_6O_2$	Benzoic Acid	189/100 mm.			
	1574	$C_{12}H_{10}O$	Phenyl ether, 100 mm.	181	176.5	27	76
A =		C_7H_8	Toluene	110.7			
	1575	C_7H_8O	p-Cresol	201.7	Nonazeotrope	v-1	213
	1576	C_7H_{14}	Methylcyclohexane	101.1	Nonazeotrope	v-1	114, 309
			" 60°-100° C.	...	Evaporation data		297
	1577	C_7H_{16}	Heptane	98	Evaporation data	v-1	114
	1578	$C_8H_{11}N$	2-Methyl-5-ethyl-pyridine	178.3	Nonazeotrope		334
	1579	C_8H_{18}	Iso-octane	...	Nonazeotrope	v-1	266
	1580	C_8H_{18}	2,2,4-Trimethylpentane	99.3	Nonazeotrope	v-1	52
	1581	$C_{10}H_{22}O$	Decyl alcohol (isomers)	217.3	Nonazeotrope		334
	1582	$C_{12}H_{26}O$	2,6,8-Trimethyl-4-nonanol	225.5	Nonazeotrope		334
A =		C_7H_8O	Benzyl Alcohol	205.2			
	1583	$C_9H_{10}O$	Benzyl vinyl ether, 25 mm.	...	103	-	341
A =		C_7H_8O	m-Cresol	202.2			
	1584	$C_9H_{10}O_2$	Ethyl benzoate	212.4	...	26.6	112

TABLE I *BINARY SYSTEMS*   **53**

		B-Component		Azeotropic Data		
No.	Formula	Name	B.P.,°C.	B.P.,°C.	Wt.%A	Ref.
A =	C_7H_8O	o-Cresol	191			
1585	$C_8H_{11}N$	s-Collidine	171.30	197.20	63.0	188
A =	C_7H_8O	x-Cresol	202			
1586	C_7H_9N	Pyridine bases	163	204.9	78	367
1587	C_7H_9N	Pyridine bases	157	204.4	80	367
1588	C_7H_9N	Pyridine bases	142-5	202.5	90	367
A =	C_7H_8O	m,p-Cresols	202			
1589	$C_{10}H_8$	Naphthalene	218.1	202	71.8	212
1590	$C_{11}H_{10}$	2-Methylnaphthalene	241.15	Nonazeotrope		98
A =	C_7H_8O	p-Cresol	201.7			
1591	$C_9H_{10}O_2$	Ethyl benzoate	212.4	...	24.5	112
A =	C_7H_9N	N-Methylaniline	196.25			
1592	$C_8H_{11}N$	N,N-Dimethyl-aniline, 95°-145°	...	Nonazeotrope	v-l	59
A =	C_7H_9N	2,6-Lutidine	143.41			
1593	$C_{10}H_{22}$	Decane	174.0	Nonazeotrope	v-l	358
A =	C_7H_9N	o-Toluidine	200.7			
1594	$C_{11}H_{17}N$	Diethyl-o-toluidine, 20 mm.	...	95.8	48	173
A =	C_7H_{14}	Methylcyclohexane	100.93			
1595	C_7H_{16}	Heptane	98	Nonazeotrope	v-l	114, 309
1596	$C_8F_{16}O$	Perfluorocyclic oxide	102.5	85	40 vol. %	207
A =	$C_7H_{14}O_2$	Heptanoic Acid	222.0			
1597	$C_9H_{19}NO$	N,N-Dimethylheptan-amide	...	Max. b.p.		295
A =	C_7H_{16}	Heptane	98			
1598	$C_8F_{18}O$	Perfluorobutyl ether	100	Min. b.p.		50
1599	C_8H_{10}	Ethylbenzene	136.15	Nonazeotrope		52
		" 100-760 mm.	...	Nonazeotrope	v-l	229
1600	C_8H_{18}	2,2,4-Trimethylpentane	99.3	Nonazeotrope		52
A =	$C_7H_{16}O_3$	Dipropylene Glycol Methyl Ether	...			
1601	$C_{11}H_{10}$	2-Methylnaphthalene	241.15	Nonazeotrope		98
A =	$C_8F_{16}O$	Perfluorocyclic Oxide	102.5			
1602	C_8H_{16}	Ethylcyclohexane	131.78	96.3	80 vol. %	207
1603	C_8H_{18}	2,2,4-Trimethylpentane	99.24	87.5	60 vol. %	207
1604	C_9H_{20}	2,3,4-Trimethylhexane	131.34	98.4	80 vol. %	207
A =	$C_8H_5Cl_3$	ar-Trichlorostyrene	...			
1605	$C_9H_{20}O_3$	2-(2-Isoamyloxyethoxy) ethanol, 6.7 mm.	...	101	...	49
A =	C_8H_8	Styrene	145			
1606	C_8H_{10}	Ethylbenzene, 10-100 mm.	...	Nonazeotrope	v-l	40, 110
		" 30°-120° C.	...	Nonazeotrope	v-l	156
1607	C_8H_{10}	Xylene, 20 mm.	50	Nonazeotrope		334
A =	$C_8H_8O_3$	Methyl Salicylate	222.3			
1608	$C_{11}H_{10}$	2-Methylnaphthalene	241.15	Nonazeotrope		98

		B-Component		Azeotropic Data		
No.	Formula	Name	B.P.,°C.	B.P.,°C.	Wt.%A	Ref.
A =	C_8H_{10}	Ethylbenzene	136.15			
1609	C_8H_{16}	Ethylcyclohexane, 400 mm.	...	Nonazeotrope	v-1	271
1610	C_8H_{16}	1-Octene	121.6	Nonazeotrope	v-1	342
1611	C_8H_{18}	Octane	125.75	Nonazeotrope		52
1612	C_9H_{12}	Cumene	152.4	Nonazeotrope		334
1613	C_9H_{20}	Nonane	150.7	Nonazeotrope		363
1614	C_9H_{20}	2,2,5-Trimethylhexane	120.1	Nonazeotrope	v-1	342
A =	C_8H_{10}	m-Xylene	139			
1615	$C_8H_{18}O$	2-Ethyl-1-hexanol	184.8	Nonazeotrope		334
1616	$C_9H_{18}O$	2-Ethylheptanal	...	139.0	96.1	52
A =	C_8H_{10}	o-Xylene	143.6			
1617	C_9H_{20}	Nonane	150.7	144.25	81	372
A =	C_8H_{10}	p-Xylene	138.4			
1618	C_8H_{18}	Octane	125.75	Nonazeotrope		52
A =	$C_8H_{14}O_3$	Bis(2-vinyloxyethyl) Ether	196.5/10 mm.			
1619	$C_8H_{18}O_3$	Bis(2-ethoxyethyl) ether, 10 mm.	187.8	Nonazeotrope	v-1	69
A =	$C_8H_{16}O_2$	1,3-Dimethylbutyl Acetate	146.1			
1620	$C_9H_{18}O$	2,6-Dimethyl-4-heptanone	169.4	Nonazeotrope		334
A =	$C_8H_{16}O_2$	2-Ethylhexanoic Acid	...			
1621	$C_{11}H_{10}$	2-Methylnaphthalene	241.15	...	<50	98
A =	$C_8H_{16}O_2$	Octanoic Acid	238.5			
1622	$C_{10}H_{21}NO$	N,N-Dimethyloctanamide, 100 mm.	187	190	26.0	295
A =	$C_8H_{16}O_3$	2-(2-Ethoxyethoxy) Ethyl Acetate	...			
1623	$C_{11}H_{10}$	2-Methylnaphthalene	241.15	Nonazeotrope		98
A =	$C_8H_{17}Cl$	3-(Chloromethyl) heptane	106.9/100 mm.			
1624	$C_8H_{18}O$	2-Ethyl-1-hexanol, 100 mm.	124.8	106	98	335
A =	$C_8H_{18}Cl_2Sn$	Dibutyltin Dichloride	157/17			
1625	$C_{12}H_{27}ClSn$	Tributyltin chloride, 17 mm.	166	Nonazeotrope		334
A =	$C_8H_{18}O$	Butyl Ether	142.1			
1626	$C_8H_{18}O$	2-Ethyl-1-hexanol	184.8	Nonazeotrope		334
A =	$C_8H_{18}O$	2-Ethyl-1-hexanol	184.8			
1627	C_9H_{20}	Nonane	150.8	Nonazeotrope		334
1628	$C_{10}H_{20}O_2$	2-Ethylhexyl acetate	198.4	Nonazeotrope		334
1629	$C_{11}H_{25}N$	(2-Ethylhexyl) propylamine, 50 mm.	147	Nonazeotrope		334
A =	$C_8H_{18}O$	Octyl Alcohol	195.15			
1630	$C_{10}H_{20}O$	Octyl vinyl ether, 5 mm.	64	64	17	341
A =	$C_8H_{18}OS$	2-Hexylthioethanol	...			
1631	$C_{10}H_{20}OS$	2-Hexylthioethyl vinyl ether	...	Min. b.p.		329

TABLE I   BINARY SYSTEMS   55

	B-Component			Azeotropic Data		
No.	Formula	Name	B.P.,°C.	B.P.,°C.	Wt.%A	Ref.
A =	$C_8H_{18}O_2$	2-Ethyl-1,3-hexanediol	243.1			
1632	$C_{16}H_{34}O$	Bis(2-ethylhexyl)ether, 10 mm.	135	123	40	335
		"	269.8	241	-	335
A =	$C_8H_{18}O_3$	2-(2-Butoxyethoxy)ethanol	231.2			
1633	$C_{10}H_8$	Naphthalene, 100 mm.	144.35	Nonazeotrope	v-l	144
1634	$C_{11}H_{10}$	1-Methylnaphthalene, 20 mm.	...	...	46.8	98
		" 100 mm.	...	...	64.3	98
		" 200 mm.	...	...	74	98
1635	$C_{11}H_{10}$	2-Methylnaphthalene, 20 mm.	...	...	38	98
		" 100 mm.	...	...	53.5	98
		"	241.15	...	82	98
1636	$C_{12}H_{26}$	Dodecane, 100 mm.	146.2	142.6	34 v-l	144
1637	$C_{15}H_{30}$	1-Pentadecene, 217 mm.	183.7	185.16	87 vol. %	291
A =	$C_9F_{21}N$	Tris(perfluoropropyl)amine	130			
1638	C_9H_{12}	Cumene	152	116	...	51
A =	$C_9H_6N_2O_2$	2,4-Tolylene Diisocyanate	...			
1639	$C_9H_6N_2O_2$	2,6-Tolylene di-isocyanate, 5-60 mm.	...	Nonazeotrope	v-l	53
A =	C_9H_7N	Isoquinoline				
1640	$C_{11}H_{10}$	2-Methylnaphthalene	241.15	...	<50	98
A =	C_9H_7N	Quinoline	237.3			
1641	$C_{11}H_{10}$	2-Methylnaphthalene	241.15	...	>50	98
A =	$C_9H_{10}O_3$	Ethyl Salicylate	233.7			
1642	$C_{12}H_{10}O$	Phenyl ether, 5 mm.	...	Nonazeotrope	v-l	118
		" 50 mm.	...	Nonazeotrope	v-l	118
		" 180 mm.	...	Nonazeotrope	v-l	118
A =	C_9H_{12}	Cumene	...			
1643	$C_{12}F_{27}N$	Tris(perfluorobutyl)amine	177	138	...	51
A =	C_9H_{12}	Mesitylene	164.7			
1644	C_9H_{12}	1,2,4-Trimethyl-benzene	169.2	Nonazeotrope		96
A =	$C_9H_{12}OS$	2-Benzylthioethanol	...			
1645	$C_{11}H_{14}OS$	2-Benzylthioethyl vinyl ether	...	Min. b.p.		329
A =	$C_9H_{14}O$	Isophorone	...			
1646	$C_{11}H_{10}$	2-Methylnaphthalene	241.15	Nonazeotrope		98
A =	C_9H_{18}	Propycyclohexane	156.72			
1647	$C_{12}F_{27}N$	Perfluorotributyl-amine	178.4	145.4	55 vol. %	207
A =	C_9H_{20}	Nonane	151			
1648	$C_{12}F_{27}N$	Perfluorotributyl-amine	177	Min. b.p.		50

		B-Component		Azeotropic Data		
No.	Formula	Name	B.P.,°C.	B.P.,°C.	Wt.%A	Ref.
A =	$C_9H_{20}O$	2,6-Dimethyl-4-heptanol	104/52			
1649	$C_{12}H_{24}$	2,6,8-Trimethyl-nonene, 8 mm.	...	56	18	334
		" 52 mm.	...	95	32	334
A =	$C_9H_{20}O_4$	Tripropylene Glycol	...			
1650	$C_{12}H_9N$	Carbazole	294	Nonazeotrope		100
		" Low press.	...	Min. b.p.		100
1651	$C_{13}H_{10}$	Fluorene, high press.	...	Min. b.p.		100
		" Low press.	...	Nonazeotrope		100
1652	$C_{14}H_{10}$	Phenanthrene	-	Min. b.p.		100
		"		% glycol decreases with decreasing pressure		100
A =	$C_{10}H_8$	Naphthalene	218.1			
1653	$C_{12}H_{26}$	Dodecane, 100 mm.	...	140.2	59.2 v-l	144, 204
A =	$C_{10}H_{18}$	Decahydronaphthalene	...			
1654	$C_{10}H_{22}$	Decane, 10 mm.	...	Nonazeotrope	v-l	309
		" 20 mm.	...	Nonazeotrope	v-l	309
		" 50 mm.	...	Nonazeotrope	v-l	309
A =	$C_{10}H_{18}O$	Menthone	209.5			
1655	$C_{10}H_{20}O$	Menthol, 5 mm.	...	Nonazeotrope	v-l	118
		" 50 mm.	...	Nonazeotrope	v-l	118
		" 180 mm.	...	Nonazeotrope	v-l	118
A =	$C_{10}H_{22}$	3,3,5-Trimethyl-heptane	155.68			
1656	$C_{12}F_{27}N$	Perfluorotributyl-amine	178.4	147.3	55 vol. %	207
A =	$C_{10}H_{22}O$	Decyl Alcohol	232.9			
1657	$C_{12}H_{26}O$	Dodecyl alcohol, 20, 50, 100, 300 mm.	...	Ideal system	v-l	290
A =	$C_{10}H_{22}OS$	2-(2-Ethylhexylthio) ethanol	...			
1658	$C_{12}H_{24}OS$	2-(2-Ethylhexylthio) ethyl vinyl ether	...	Min. b.p.		329
A =	$C_{10}H_{22}O_4$	Tripropylene Glycol Methyl Ether	...			
1659	$C_{11}H_{10}$	2-Methylnaphthalene	241.15	...	<50	98
A =	$C_{11}H_{10}$	1-Methylnaphthalene	244.8			
1660	$C_{11}H_{24}O$	5-Ethyl-2-nonanol, 19 mm.	...	121	41.4	98, 99
		" 50 mm.	...	143	25.2	98, 99
		" 150 mm.	...	173	5.25	98, 99
		" 200 mm.	...	179.5	2	98, 99
		" 400 mm.	...	Nonazeotrope		98, 99
A =	$C_{11}H_{10}$	2-Methylnaphthalene	241.1			
1661	$C_{11}H_{24}O$	5-Ethyl-2-nonanol, 20 mm.	...	120	49.8	98, 99
		" 50 mm.	...	140.5	36.0	98, 99
		" 90 mm.	...	157	24.5	98, 99
		" 200 mm.	...	181.5	9.0	98, 99
		" 300 mm.	...	193.5	3.5	98, 99
		" 400 mm.	...	Nonazeotrope		98, 99

TABLE I *BINARY SYSTEMS* **57**

		B-Component		Azeotropic Data			
No.	Formula	Name	B.P.,°C.	B.P.,°C.	Wt.%A		Ref.
A =	$C_{12}H_9N$	Carbazole	355				
1662	$C_{14}H_{30}O$	Tetradecanol	...	Nonazeotrope			100
	"	" Low press.	...	Min. b.p.			100
1663	$C_{17}H_{36}O$	Heptadecanol	...	Nonazeotrope			100
	"	" Low press.	...	Min. b.p.			100
A =	$C_{12}H_{10}$	Biphenyl	255.9				
1664	$C_{24}H_{38}O_4$	Dioctyl phthalate, 10 mm.	248	Nonazeotrope			334
A =	$C_{12}H_{24}$	2,6,8-Trimethylnonene	...				
1665	$C_{12}H_{26}O$	2,6,8-Trimethyl-4-nonanol, 50 mm.	137	Nonazeotrope			334
	"	" 10 mm.	103	Nonazeotrope			334
A =	$C_{12}H_{26}$	Dodecane	216				
1666	$C_{16}H_{34}$	Hexadecane, 10-760 mm.	...	Nonazeotrope		v-l	163
A =	$C_{13}H_{10}$	Fluorene	294				
1667	$C_{14}H_{30}O$	Tetradecanol, Low press.	...	Nonazeotrope			100
	"	" High press.	...	Min. b.p.			100
1668	$C_{17}H_{36}O$	Heptadecanol, Low press.	...	Nonazeotrope			100
	"	" High press.	...	Min. b.p.			100
A =	$C_{14}H_{10}$	Phenanthrene	340				
1669	$C_{14}H_{30}O$	Tetradecanol	...	% Phenanthrene increases with pressure; min. b.p.			100
1670	$C_{17}H_{36}O$	Heptadecanol	...	% Phenanthrene increases with pressure; min. b.p.			100
A =	$C_{16}H_{32}O_2$	Palmitic Acid	...				
1671	$C_{18}H_{36}O_2$	Stearic acid, 5 mm.	...	...	...	v-l	139
A =	$C_{18}H_{34}O_2$	Oleic Acid	...				
1672	$C_{18}H_{34}O_3$	Ricinoleic acid, 5 mm.	...	...	...	v-l	139
1673	$C_{18}H_{36}O_2$	Stearic acid, 5 mm.	...	...	...	v-l	139
1674	$C_{20}H_{30}O_2$	Abietic acid, 1-10 mm.	...	Nonazeotrope		v-l	166

Table II. Ternary Systems

No.	A-Component Formula	Name	B.P., °C.	B-Component Formula	Name	B.P., °C.	C-Component Formula	Name	B.P., °C.	B.P., °C.		Azeotropic Data Composition, Wt.% A	B	C	Ref.
1675	A	Argon	-185.7	N_2	Nitrogen	-195.8	O_2	Oxygen	-183	...	v-1	Nonazeotrope			97,194
1676[a]	CO	Carbon monoxide	-192	H_2	Hydrogen	-252.7	N_2	Nitrogen	-195.8	...	v-1	Nonazeotrope			2
1677	ClF_3	Chlorine trifluoride	...	FH	Hydrogen fluoride	19.4	F_6U	Uranium hexafluoride	56	...	v-1	Nonazeotrope			91,292
1678	ClH	Hydrogen chloride	-85	C_5H_5N	Pyridine	115.5	$C_{10}H_8$	Naphthalene	218.1	189.6		...	...	...	322
1679	HF	Hydrogen fluoride	19.5	H_2O	Water	100	$C_4HF_7O_2$	Perfluorobutyric acid	...	108		12	28	60	222
1680	HNO_3	Nitric acid	...	H_2O	Water	100	$CHCl_3$	Chloroform	61	...	v-1	92	3	5	258
1681	H_2O	Water	100	SO_2	Sulfur dioxide	-10	C_2H_4O	Acetaldehyde	20.2	...	v-1	Nonazeotrope			273
1682	H_2O	Water	100	$CHCl_3$	Chloroform	61	CH_2O_2	Formic acid	100.75	...	v-1	Nonazeotrope			56
1683	H_2O	Water	100	$CHCl_3$	Chloroform	61	CH_4O	Methanol	64.7	52.6		4	81	15	335
1684	H_2O	Water	100	$CHCl_3$	Chloroform	61	C_2H_3N	Acetonitrile	81.6	...	v-1	Nonazeotrope			334
1685	H_2O	Water	100	$CHCl_3$	Chloroform	61	$C_2H_4O_2$	Acetic acid	118.1	78.0		3.9	91.2	4.9	56
1686[b]	H_2O	Water	100	$CHCl_3$	Chloroform	61	C_2H_6O	Ethyl alcohol	78.3	...		Nonazeotrope			335
1687	H_2O	Water	100	$CHCl_3$	Chloroform	61	C_4H_8O	2-Butanone	79.6	...	v-1	Nonazeotrope			334
1688	H_2O	Water	100	CH_2O_2	Formic acid	100.75	$C_2H_4O_2$	Acetic acid	118.1	...		Nonazeotrope			56
1689	H_2O	Water	100	CH_2O_2	Formic acid	100.75	C_5H_5N	Pyridine	115.5	...		Nonazeotrope			360
1690	H_2O	Water	100	CH_3NO_2	Nitromethane	101	C_3H_8O	Isopropyl alcohol	82.3	...	v-1	11.7	36.8	51.5	176
1691	H_2O	Water	100	CH_4O	Methanol	64.3	$C_2Cl_3F_3$	1,1,2-Trichlorotrifluoroethane	47.5	39.4		0.6	3.0	96.4	335
1692	H_2O	Water	100	CH_4O	Methanol	64.7	C_2H_6O	Ethyl alcohol	78.3	...	v-1	Nonazeotrope			68
1693	H_2O	Water	100	CH_4O	Methanol	64.7	C_3H_6O	Propionaldehyde	47.9	...		Nonazeotrope			334
1694	H_2O	Water	100	CH_4O	Methanol	64.7	$C_3H_6O_2$	Methyl acetate	57.1	...	v-1	Nonazeotrope			58
1695	H_2O	Water	100	CH_4O	Methanol	64.7	C_3H_8O	Isopropyl alcohol	82.3	...		Nonazeotrope			334

[a] 20 atm. to critical point.
[b] 20 p.s.i.g.

No.	A-Component Formula	A-Component Name	A-Component B.P. °C	B-Component Formula	B-Component Name	B-Component B.P. °C	C-Component Formula	C-Component Name	C-Component B.P. °C	Azeotropic Data B.P. °C	Composition, Wt.% A	B	C	Ref.
1696	H_2O	Water	100	CH_4O	Methanol	64.7	$C_4H_6O_2$	Methyl acrylate	80.9	Nonazeotrope				334
1697	H_2O	Water	100	CH_4O	Methanol	64.7	$C_4H_8O_2$	Methyl propionate	79.85	Nonazeotrope				84
1698	H_2O	Water	100	CH_4O	Methanol	64.7	C_4H_{10}	2-Methyl-propane	-11.7	Nonazeotrope				334
1699	H_2O	Water	100	$C_2Cl_3F_3$	1,1,2-Tri-chlorotri-fluoroethane	47.5	C_2H_6O	Ethyl alcohol	78.3	42.6	0.6	3.9	95.5	335
1700	H_2O	Water	100	C_2HCl_3	Trichloro-ethylene	86.2	C_3H_6O	Allyl alcohol	97.1	71.4	7.5	80	12.5	334
1701	H_2O	Water	100	C_2HCl_3	Trichloro-ethylene	86.2	C_3H_8O	Propyl alcohol	97.3	...	7.1	84.8	8.1	176
1702	H_2O	Water	100	C_2HCl_3	Trichloro-ethylene	86.2	C_3H_8O	Isopropyl alcohol	82.3	69.4	7	73	20	335
1703	H_2O	Water	100	C_2H_3N	Acetonitrile	81.6	C_2H_6O	Ethyl alcohol	78.3	72.9	1	44	55	335
1704	H_2O	Water	100	C_2H_3N	Acetonitrile	81.6	$C_4H_{11}N$	Diethylamine	55.5	Nonazeotrope				334
1705	H_2O	Water	100	C_2H_3N	Acetonitrile	81.6	$C_6H_{14}O$	Isopropyl ether	68.3	59	5	13	82	334
1706	H_2O	Water	100	C_2H_3N	Acetonitrile	81.6	$C_6H_{15}N$	Triethylamine	89.7	68.6	6	31	63	334
1707	H_2O	Water	100	$C_2H_4Cl_2$	1,2-Dichloro-ethane	83.5	C_2H_6O	Ethyl alcohol	78.3	67.8	7.2	77.1	15.7	335
1708	H_2O	Water	100	$C_2H_4Cl_2$	1,2-Dichloro-ethane	83.5	C_3H_8O	Isopropyl alcohol	82.3	69.7	7.7	73.3	19.0	335
1709	H_2O	Water	100	C_2H_4O	Acetalde-hyde	20.2	C_2H_6O	Ethyl alcohol	78.3	...	...	...	v-1	133
1710	H_2O	Water	100	C_2H_4O	Acetalde-hyde	20.2	$C_6H_{12}O_3$	Paraldehyde	124	Nonazeotrope				334
1711	H_2O	Water	100	C_2H_5ClO	2-Chloro-ethanol	128.7	C_6H_6	Benzene	80.1	Nonazeotrope				334
1712	H_2O	Water	100	C_2H_6O	Ethyl alcohol	78.3	C_3H_3N	Acrylonitrile	77.2	69.5	8.7	20.3	71.0	335
	H_2O	Water	100		Ethyl alcohol			Acrylonitrile	100 mm.	<30	6.6	9.0	84.4	335
1713	H_2O	Water	100	C_2H_6O	Ethyl alcohol	78.3	C_3H_6O	Acetone	56.1	Nonazeotrope				334
1714	H_2O	Water	100	C_2H_6C	Ethyl alcohol	78.3	$C_3H_6O_2$	Ethyl formate	54.2	Nonazeotrope				334
1715	H_2O	Water	100	C_2H_6O	Ethyl alcohol	78.3	C_4H_6O	Crotonalde-hyde	102.4	78.0	4.8	87.9	7.3	335

TABLE II   **TERNARY SYSTEMS**   61

No.	A-Component Formula	A-Component Name	B.P., °C	B-Component Formula	B-Component Name	B.P., °C	C-Component Formula	C-Component Name	B.P., °C	Azeotropic Data B.P., °C	Composition, Wt.% A	B	C	Ref.
1716	H₂O	Water	100	C₂H₆O	Ethyl alcohol	78.3	C₄H₈O	2-Butanone	79.6	73.2	11	14	75	335
1717	H₂O	Water	100	C₂H₆O	Ethyl alcohol	78.3	C₄H₈O	Butyraldehyde	75.7	67.2	9	11	80	335
1718	H₂O	Water	100	C₂H₆O	Ethyl alcohol	78.3	C₄H₈O	Ethyl vinyl ether	35.5	Nonazeotrope				334
1719	H₂O	Water	100	C₂H₆O	Ethyl alcohol	78.3	C₄H₁₁N	Butylamine	77.8	81.8	7.5	42.5	50.0	335
1720	H₂O	Water	100	C₂H₆O	Ethyl alcohol	78.3	C₅H₈O₂	Ethyl acrylate	99.3	77.1	10.1	48.3	41.6	335
								"	165 mm.	44	8.6	36.3	55.1	335
1721	H₂O	Water	100	C₂H₆O	Ethyl alcohol	78.3	C₅H₁₀O	1-Butenyl methyl ether	...	61.4	6.8	14.3	78.9	334
1722	H₂O	Water	100	C₂H₆O	Ethyl alcohol	78.3	C₅H₁₀O	Propyl vinyl ether	65.1	57	5.1	21.2	73.7	335
1723	H₂O	Water	100	C₂H₆O	Ethyl alcohol	78.3	C₅H₁₀O₂	Isopropyl acetate	88.7	74.8	9.8	19.4	70.8	335
1724	H₂O	Water	100	C₂H₆O	Ethyl alcohol	78.3	C₅H₁₂O	Butyl methyl ether	70.3	62	6.3	8.6	85.1	335
1725	H₂O	Water	100	C₂H₆O	Ethyl alcohol	78.3	C₅H₁₂O	Isoamyl alcohol	132	Nonazeotrope v-1				218
1726	H₂O	Water	100	C₂H₆O	Ethyl alcohol	78.3	C₆H₁₂	Cyclohexane	80.75	62.60	4.8	19.7	75.5	361
								"	80.7	62.1	7	17	76	335
1727	H₂O	Water	100	C₂H₆O	Ethyl alcohol	78.3	C₆H₁₂O	Isobutyl vinyl ether	83.4	60	8	22	70	335
1728	H₂O	Water	100	C₂H₆O	Ethyl alcohol	78.3	C₆H₁₄	Hexane	68.22	56.4	3	18.7	78.3	326
								"	68.7	56.0	3	12	85	335
1729	H₂O	Water	100	C₂H₆O	Ethyl alcohol	78.3	C₆H₁₄O	Butyl ethyl ether	92.2	71.6	9.3	4.2	86.5	335
1730	H₂O	Water	100	C₂H₆O	Ethyl alcohol	78.3	C₆H₁₄O	Ethyl iso-butyl ether	79	66	6.5	15.8	77.7	334
1731	H₂O	Water	100	C₂H₆O	Ethyl alcohol	78.3	C₆H₁₄O	Isopropyl ether	68.3	61.0	4.0	6.5	89.5	335
								"	100 p.s.i.g.	128.5 p.s.i.g.	9.1	14.2	76.7	335
								"	50 p.s.i.g.	105.8 p.s.i.g.	7.1	11.9	81	335
1732	H₂O	Water	100	C₂H₆O	Ethyl alcohol	78.3	C₆H₁₄O	Isopropyl propyl ether	66	66	7.0	14.7	78.3	334
1733	H₂O	Water	100	C₂H₆O	Ethyl alcohol	78.3	C₇H₈	Toluene	110.6	74.4	12	37	51	335
1734	H₂O	Water	100	C₂H₆O	Ethyl alcohol	78.3	C₇H₁₄	Methylcyclohexane	100.88	69.59	6.8	32.4	60.8	326
1735	H₂O	Water	100	C₂H₆O	Ethyl alcohol	78.3	C₇H₁₆	Heptane	98.4	68.8	6.1	33.0	60.9	335
1736	H₂O	Water	100	C₂H₆O	Ethyl alcohol	78.3	C₈H₈	Styrene	145.1	Nonazeotrope				334

No.	A-Component Formula	A-Component Name	A-Component B.P., °C.	B-Component Formula	B-Component Name	B-Component B.P., °C.	C-Component Formula	C-Component Name	C-Component B.P., °C.	Azeotropic Data B.P., °C.	Composition, Wt. % A	B	C	Ref.
1737	H_2O	Water	100	C_2H_6O	Ethyl alcohol	78.3	$C_8H_{18}O$	Butyl ether	142.1		Nonazeotrope			334
1738	H_2O	Water	100	C_2H_6O	Ethyl alcohol	78.3	$C_8H_{18}O_2$	2-Ethyl-1,3-hexanediol	243.1		Nonazeotrope			334
1739	H_2O	Water	100	C_2H_7N	Dimethylamine	7.4	$C_4H_{11}NO$	2-(Dimethylamino)ethanol	134.6		Nonazeotrope			334
1740	H_2O	Water	100	$C_2H_8N_2$	Ethylenediamine	116.9	C_6H_6	Benzene	80.1		Nonazeotrope			334
1741	H_2O	Water	100	C_3H_3N	Acrylonitrile	77.2	C_3H_5N	Propionitrile	97.4		Nonazeotrope			334
1742	H_2O	Water	100	C_3H_4O	2-Propyn-1-ol	115	$C_5H_8O_2$	3,3-Dimethoxypropyne	111	88.95	...	...	...	95
1743	H_2O	Water	100	C_3H_4O	2-Propyn-1-ol	115	C_6H_6	Benzene	80.1	68.1	8.3	3.7	88.0	52
										69	9	4	87	95
1744	H_2O	Water	100	$C_3H_4O_2$	Acrylic acid	141.2	$C_5H_8O_2$	Ethyl acrylate	99.3		Nonazeotrope			334
1745	H_2O	Water	100	$C_3H_6Cl_2$	1,2-Dichloropropane	96.3	C_3H_7ClO	Propylene chlorohydrin	127.4		Nonazeotrope			334
1746	H_2O	Water	100	C_3H_6O	Acetone	56.1	C_3H_8O	Isopropyl alcohol	82.3		Nonazeotrope		v-l	46
1747	H_2O	Water	100	C_3H_6O	Acetone	56.1	$C_4H_6O_2$	Vinyl acetate	72.7		Nonazeotrope			334
1748	H_2O	Water	100	C_3H_6O	Acetone	56.1	C_4H_8O	2-Butanone	79.6		Nonazeotrope			254
1749	H_2O	Water	100	C_3H_6O	Acetone	56.1	C_4H_8O	Butyraldehyde	74.8		Nonazeotrope			334
1750	H_2O	Water	100	C_3H_6O	Acetone	56.1	$C_5H_{10}O_2$	Isopropyl acetate	88.6		Nonazeotrope			334
1751[c]	H_2O	Water	100	C_3H_6O	Acetone	56.1	$C_6H_{14}O$	Isopropyl ether	68.3	75	3	49	48	334
1752	H_2O	Water	100	C_3H_6O	Acetone	56.1	C_nH_{2n+2}	Paraffin hydrochloride	...	61-71	1.4	42.1	56.5 vol. %	169
1753	H_2O	Water	100	C_3H_6O	Allyl alcohol	96.6	C_6H_{14}	Hexane	68.8	...	8.5	5.1	86.4	176
1754	H_2O	Water	100	C_3H_6O	Allyl alcohol	96.6	C_7H_8	Toluene	110.6	80.6	15.2	31.4	53.4	334
1755	H_2O	Water	100	C_3H_6O	Allyl alcohol	96.6	$C_9H_{16}O_2$	2,2-Bis(allyloxy) propane	...	88	28	55	17	334

[c] 15 p.s.i.g.

TABLE II   TERNARY SYSTEMS   63

No.	A-Component Formula	A-Component Name	A B.P. °C.	B-Component Formula	B-Component Name	B B.P. °C.	C-Component Formula	C-Component Name	C B.P. °C.	Azeotrope B.P. °C.	Comp. Wt.% A	B	C	Ref.
1756	H_2O	Water	100	$C_3H_6O_2$	Propionic acid	140.7	$C_4H_8O_2$	Methyl propionate	79.85	Nonazeotrope				84
1757	H_2O	Water	100	C_3H_8O	Isopropyl alcohol	82.3	C_4H_8O	2-Butanone	79.6	73.4	11	1	88	335
1758	H_2O	Water	100	C_3H_8O	Isopropyl alcohol	82.3	$C_4H_{11}N$	Butylamine	77.8	83	12.5	40.5	47	335
1759	H_2O	Water	100	C_3H_8O	Isopropyl alcohol	82.3	$C_5H_{10}O_2$	Isopropyl acetate	88.7	75.5	11	13	76	335
1760	H_2O	Water	100	C_3H_8O	Isopropyl alcohol	82.3	C_6H_6	Benzene	80.1	65.7	8.2	19.8	72.0	335
		"			"			"	20 p.s.i.g.	90	10	18	72	335
1761	H_2O	Water	100	C_3H_8O	Isopropyl alcohol	82.3	$C_6H_{12}O$	4-Methyl-2-pentanone	116.2	Nonazeotrope				334
1762	H_2O	Water	100	C_3H_8O	Isopropyl alcohol	82.3	$C_6H_{14}O$	Butyl ethyl ether	92.2	73.4	10.4	21.9	67.7	335
1763	H_2O	Water	100	C_3H_8O	Isopropyl alcohol	82.3	$C_6H_{14}O$	Isopropyl ether	68.3	61.8	5	4	91	335
		"			"			"	30 p.s.i.g.	95	6	9	85	335
		"			"			"	15 p.s.i.g.	81	6	7	87	334
1764	H_2O	Water	100	C_3H_8O	Isopropyl alcohol	82.3	$C_6H_{15}N$	Diisopropyl-amine	84.1	Nonazeotrope				335
1765	H_2O	Water	100	C_3H_8O	Isopropyl alcohol	82.3	C_7H_8	Toluene	110.6	76.3	13.1	38.2	48.7	335
1766	H_2O	Water	100	C_3H_8O	Isopropyl alcohol	82.3	C_8H_{14}	Diisobutyl-ene	102.3	72.3	9.3	31.6	59.1	335
1767[d]	H_2O	Water	100	C_3H_8O	Propyl alcohol	97.3	C_3H_8S	1-Propane-thiol	67.5	60.8	...	...	...	181
1768	H_2O	Water	100	C_3H_8O	Propyl alcohol	97.3	$C_5H_{10}O$	3-Pentanone	101.8	81.2	20	20	60	334
1769	H_2O	Water	100	C_3H_8O	Propyl alcohol	97.3	$C_5H_{10}O_2$	Propyl acetate	101.6	Nonazeotrope				264
		"			"			"	200 mm.	50.23	13.3	4.7	82.0 v-1	308
		"			"			"	400 mm.	66.07	15.0	6.5	78.5 v-1	308
		"			"			"	600 mm.	76.26	16.0	8.5	75.5 v-1	308
		"			"			"	760 mm.	82.45	17.0	10.0	73.0 v-1	308
1770	H_2O	Water	100	C_3H_8O	Propyl alcohol	97.3	C_6H_6	Benzene	80.1	68.5	8.6	9.0	82.4	334
1771	H_2O	Water	100	C_3H_8O	Propyl alcohol	97.3	C_6H_{12}	Cyclohexane	80.7	66.6	8.5	10.0	81.5	334

[d] 771 mm.

No.	A-Component Formula	Name	B.P., °C	B-Component Formula	Name	B.P., °C	C-Component Formula	Name	B.P., °C	Azeotropic Data B.P., °C	Composition, Wt.% A	B	C	Ref.
1772	H_2O	Water	100	C_3H_8O	Propyl alcohol	97.3	$C_6H_{12}O$	2-Hexanone	127.2	87	27	63	10	123
1773	H_2O	Water	100	C_3H_8O	Propyl alcohol	97.3	$C_6H_{12}O$	2-Methylpentanal	118.3	86	28	58	14	334
1774	H_2O	Water	100	C_3H_8O	Propyl alcohol	97.3	$C_7H_{16}O_2$	Dipropoxyethane	146.6	87.6	27.4	51.6	21.0	334
1775	H_2O	Water	100	$C_3H_8O_2$	2-Methoxyethanol	124.6	C_6H_6	Benzene	80.1	Nonazeotrope				334
1776	H_2O	Water	100	$C_3H_8O_2$	2-Methoxyethanol	124.6	C_6H_{12}	Cyclohexane	80.7	Nonazeotrope				334
1777	H_2O	Water	100	$C_3H_8O_2$	2-Methoxyethanol	124.6	C_7H_8	Toluene	110.6	Nonazeotrope				334
1778	H_2O	Water	100	$C_3H_8O_2$	1,2-Propanediol	187.8	C_7H_8	Toluene	110.6	Nonazeotrope				334
1779	H_2O	Water	100	C_4H_6O	Crotonaldehyde	102.4	$C_6H_{10}O$	2-Ethylcrotonaldehyde	135.3	Nonazeotrope				334
1780	H_2O	Water	100	C_4H_8O	2-Butanone	79.6	C_6H_6	Benzene	80.1	68.2	8.8	26.1	65.1	334
1781	H_2O	Water	100	C_4H_8O	2-Butanone	79.6	C_6H_{12}	Cyclohexane	80.7	63.6	5	35	60	334
1782	H_2O	Water	100	C_4H_8O	2-Butanone	79.6	C_6H_{14}	Hexane	68.7	55	1	22	77	334
1783	H_2O	Water	100	C_4H_8O	Butyraldehyde	74.8	$C_4H_{10}O$	Isobutyl alcohol	107.9	Nonazeotrope				334
1784	H_2O	Water	100	C_4H_8O	Butyraldehyde	74.8	$C_4H_{10}O_2$	1,1-Dimethoxyethane	64.5	Nonazeotrope				334
1785	H_2O	Water	100	C_4H_8O	Butyraldehyde	74.8	$C_6H_{12}O_2$	Butyl acetate	126.1	Nonazeotrope				334
1786	H_2O	Water	100	C_4H_8O	Butyraldehyde	74.8	C_6H_{14}	Hexane	68.7	55	4	21	75	334
1787	H_2O	Water	100	$C_4H_{10}O$	Butyl alcohol	117.7	$C_4H_{10}O$	sec-Butyl alcohol	99.5	Nonazeotrope				334
1788	H_2O	Water	100	$C_4H_{10}O$	Butyl alcohol	117.7	$C_4H_{10}S$	1-Butanethiol	97.5	78.6	...	...	...	181
1789	H_2O	Water	100	$C_4H_{10}O$	Butyl alcohol	117.7	$C_4H_{11}N$	Butylamine	77.8	Nonazeotrope				334
1790	H_2O	Water	100	$C_4H_{10}O$	Butyl alcohol	117.75	$C_6H_{12}O$	Butyl vinyl ether	94.2	77.4	10	2	88	335
1791	H_2O	Water	100	$C_4H_{10}O$	Butyl alcohol	117.75	$C_6H_{12}O_2$	Butyl acetate	126.1	90.7	29	8	63	335
1792	H_2O	Water	100	$C_4H_{10}O$	Butyl alcohol	117.75	C_6H_{14}	Hexane	68.95	61.5	19.2	2.9	77.9	174

TABLE II   TERNARY SYSTEMS 65

No.	\[A\] Formula	\[A\] Name	\[A\] B.P., °C	\[B\] Formula	\[B\] Name	\[B\] B.P., °C	\[C\] Formula	\[C\] Name	\[C\] B.P., °C	Azeo B.P., °C	Comp Wt.% A	Comp Wt.% B	Comp Wt.% C	Ref.
1793	H_2O	Water	100	$C_4H_{10}O$	Butyl alcohol	117.75	$C_7H_{12}O_2$	Butyl acrylate	147	92	50	37.6	12.4	76
1794	H_2O	Water	100	$C_4H_{10}O$	Butyl alcohol	117.75	C_7H_{16}	Heptane	98.4, 100 mm.	46	41	26	33	335
1795	H_2O	Water	100	$C_4H_{10}O$	Butyl alcohol	117.75	C_8H_{18}	Octane	125.75	78.1	41.4	7.6	51	174
1795	H_2O	Water	100	$C_4H_{10}O$	Butyl alcohol	117.75	C_8H_{18}	Octane	125.75	86.1	60	14.6	25.4	174
1796	H_2O	Water	100	$C_4H_{10}O$	Butyl alcohol	117.75	$C_8H_{18}O$	Butyl ether	142.1, 100 mm.	90.6	29.9	34.6	35.5	335
1796	H_2O	Water	100	$C_4H_{10}O$	Butyl alcohol	117.75	$C_8H_{18}O$	Butyl ether	142.1, 100 mm.	45	31.2	24.6	44.2	335
1797	H_2O	Water	100	$C_4H_{10}O$	Butyl alcohol	117.75	$C_8H_{19}N$	Dibutyl-amine	159.6	Nonazeotrope				334
1798	H_2O	Water	100	$C_4H_{10}O$	Butyl alcohol	117.75	C_9H_{20}	Nonane	150.7	90	69.9	18.3	11.8	174
1799	H_2O	Water	100	$C_4H_{10}O$	Butyl alcohol	117.75	$C_9H_{20}O_2$	Dibutoxy-methane	181.8	Nonazeotrope				334
1800	H_2O	Water	100	$C_4H_{10}O$	sec-Butyl alcohol	99.4	$C_4H_{10}O$	tert-Butyl alcohol	82.6	Nonazeotrope				334
1801	H_2O	Water	100	$C_4H_{10}O$	sec-Butyl alcohol	99.4	C_6H_6	Benzene	80.1, 200 mm.	38.2	7	5	88	67
1801	H_2O	Water	100	$C_4H_{10}O$	sec-Butyl alcohol	99.4	C_6H_6	Benzene	300 mm.	47.0	7	6	87	67
1801	H_2O	Water	100	$C_4H_{10}O$	sec-Butyl alcohol	99.4	C_6H_6	Benzene	400 mm.	53.8	7	6	87	67
1801	H_2O	Water	100	$C_4H_{10}O$	sec-Butyl alcohol	99.4	C_6H_6	Benzene	500 mm.	59.0	7	6	87	67
1801	H_2O	Water	100	$C_4H_{10}O$	sec-Butyl alcohol	99.4	C_6H_6	Benzene	665 mm.	65.5	8	6	86	67
1802	H_2O	Water	100	$C_4H_{10}O$	sec-Butyl alcohol	99.4	$C_6H_{12}O_2$	sec-Butyl acetate	112.2	85.5	20.2	27.4	52.4	334
1803	H_2O	Water	100	$C_4H_{10}O$	sec-Butyl alcohol	99.4	C_7H_{14}	Methyl-cyclohexane	101.1	77.1	11.9	21.9	66.4	352
1804	H_2O	Water	100	$C_4H_{10}O$	sec-Butyl alcohol	99.4	C_7H_{16}	Heptane	98.4	75.8	10.9	22.2	66.9	352
1805	H_2O	Water	100	$C_4H_{10}O$	sec-Butyl alcohol	99.4	C_8H_{14}	Diisobutyl-ene	102.3	77.5	11	19	70	334
1806	H_2O	Water	100	$C_4H_{10}O$	sec-Butyl alcohol	99.4	C_8H_{18}	Iso-octane	...	76.3	10.6	21.9	67.5	352
1807	H_2O	Water	100	$C_4H_{10}O$	sec-Butyl alcohol	99.4	$C_8H_{18}O$	Butyl ether	142.1	86.6	24.7	56.1	19.2	334
1808	H_2O	Water	100	$C_4H_{10}O$	Isobutyl alcohol	107.9	$C_9H_{20}O_2$	Diisobutoxy-methane	163.8	Nonazeotrope				334
1809	H_2O	Water	100	$C_4H_{10}O_2$	2-Ethoxy-ethanol	135.6	C_7H_8	Toluene	110.7	Nonazeotrope				334
1810	H_2O	Water	100	$C_4H_{10}O_2$	2-Ethoxy-ethanol	135.6	$C_{10}H_{20}O$	2-Ethylhexyl vinyl ether	177.7	97.7	51	11	38	334

No.	A-Component Formula	A-Component Name	A B.P. °C	B-Component Formula	B-Component Name	B B.P. °C	C-Component Formula	C-Component Name	C B.P. °C	Azeotropic Data B.P. °C	Comp. Wt.% A	Comp. Wt.% B	Comp. Wt.% C	Ref.
1811	H_2O	Water	100	$C_4H_{11}N$	Butylamine	77.8	$C_8H_{19}N$	Dibutylamine	159.6	Nonazeotrope				334
1812	H_2O	Water	100	$C_4H_{11}N$	Diethylamine	55.5	$C_6H_{14}O$	Isopropyl ether	68.3	Nonazeotrope				334
1813	H_2O	Water	100	C_5H_5N	Pyridine	115.5	C_7H_{16}	Heptane	98.4	78.6	14	13.5	70.5	332
1814	H_2O	Water	100	C_5H_5N	Pyridine	115.5	C_8H_{18}	Octane	125.75	86.7	22.5	25.5	52	332
1815	H_2O	Water	100	C_5H_5N	Pyridine	115.5	C_9H_{20}	Nonane	150.7	90.5	30.5	37	32.5	332
1816	H_2O	Water	100	C_5H_5N	Pyridine	115.5	$C_{10}H_{22}$	Decane	173.3	92.3	35.5	45.5	19	332
1817	H_2O	Water	100	C_5H_5N	Pyridine	115.5	$C_{11}H_{24}$	Undecane	194.5	93.1	38.5	51	10.5	332
1818	H_2O	Water	100	C_5H_5N	Pyridine	115.5	$C_{12}H_{26}$	Dodecane	216	93.5	40.5	54.5	5	332
1819	H_2O	Water	100	$C_5H_8O_2$	Ethyl acrylate	99.3	$C_6H_{14}O$	Isopropyl ether	68.3	Nonazeotrope				334
1820	H_2O	Water	100	$C_5H_{10}O$	2-Pentanone	102.3	C_6H_6	Benzene	80.1	Nonazeotrope				334
1821	H_2O	Water	100	$C_5H_{12}O$	Amyl alcohol	138.0	$C_{11}H_{24}O$	Diamyloxymethane	...	Nonazeotrope				334
1822[e]	H_2O	Water	100	$C_5H_{12}O$	Isoamyl alcohol	132	$C_5H_{12}S$	3-Methyl-1-butanethiol	120	86.6	...	...	...	181
1823	H_2O	Water	100	C_6H_6	Benzene	80.1	$C_6H_{14}O$	Hexyl alcohol	157.85	Nonazeotrope				176
1824	H_2O	Water	100	C_6H_7N	2-Picoline	128.8	$C_6H_{12}O_3$	Paraldehyde	124.5	Nonazeotrope				334
1825	H_2O	Water	100	$C_6H_{10}O$	Cyclohexanone	155.6	$C_6H_{12}O$	Cyclohexanol	160.65	Nonazeotrope		v-l		122
1826	H_2O	Water	100	$C_6H_{12}O_2$	Butyl acetate	126.1	$C_6H_{12}O_2$	sec-Butyl acetate	112.2	Nonazeotrope				334
1827	H_2O	Water	100	$C_6H_{12}O_2$	Butyl acetate	126.1	$C_8H_{18}O$	Butyl ether	142.1	Nonazeotrope				334
1828	H_2O	Water	100	$C_6H_{12}O_2$	sec-Butyl acetate	112.2	$C_8H_{18}O$	Butyl ether	142.1	Nonazeotrope				334
1829	H_2O	Water	100	$C_6H_{12}O_3$	2-Ethoxyethyl acetate	156.2	C_7H_8	Toluene	110.6	Nonazeotrope				334
1830	H_2O	Water	100	$C_6H_{14}O$	Isopropyl ether	68.3	$C_6H_{15}N$	Triethylamine	89.7	Nonazeotrope				334
1831	H_2O	Water	100	C_7H_8	Toluene	110.6	$C_{10}H_{22}O$	Decyl alcohol (isomers)	217.3	Nonazeotrope				334

[e] 765.4 mm.

TABLE II   TERNARY SYSTEMS   67

No.	A-Component Formula	A-Component Name	A B.P. °C	B-Component Formula	B-Component Name	B B.P. °C	C-Component Formula	C-Component Name	C B.P. °C	Azeo. B.P. °C	Composition, Wt.% A	B	C		Ref.
1832	H_2O	Water	100	C_7H_8	Toluene	110.6	$C_{12}H_{26}O$	2,6,8-Trimethyl-4-nonanol	225.5		Nonazeotrope				334
1833	CCl_4	Carbon tetrachloride	76.75	C_2HCl_3	Trichloroethylene	86.2	C_4H_8O	2-Butanone	79.6		Nonazeotrope			v-l	184
1834	$CHCl_3$	Chloroform	61	CH_2O_2	Formic acid	100.75	$C_2H_4O_2$	Acetic acid	118.1		Nonazeotrope			v-l	56
1835	$CHCl_3$	Chloroform	61	CH_4O	Methanol	64.7	C_3H_6O	Acetone	56.1	57.5	46.7	23.4	29.9	v-l	335
1836	$CHCl_3$	Chloroform	61	CH_4O	Methanol	64.7	$C_3H_6O_2$	Methyl acetate	57.1	56.42	51.4	21.6	27	v-l	31,143
1837	$CHCl_3$	Chloroform	61	CH_4O	Methanol	64.7	C_4H_8O	2-Butanone	79.6		Nonazeotrope				334
1838	$CHCl_3$	Chloroform	61	C_2H_6O	Ethyl alcohol	78.3	C_3H_6O	Acetone	56.1	63.2	65.3	10.4	24.3	v-l	224
1839	$CHCl_3$	Chloroform	61	C_3H_6O	Acetone	56.4	C_4H_8O	2-Butanone	79.6		Nonazeotrope			v-l	62
1840	$CHCl_3$	Chloroform	61	C_3H_6O	Acetone	56.4	$C_6H_{12}O$	4-Methyl-2-pentanone	115.9		Nonazeotrope			v-l	157
1841	$CHCl_3$	Chloroform	61	C_3H_6O	Acetone	56.4	$C_6H_{14}O$	Isopropyl ether	68.3		Nonazeotrope				334
1842	$CHCl_3$	Chloroform	61	C_2H_6O	Acetone	56.4	C_7H_8	Toluene	110.7		Nonazeotrope			v-l	296
1843	$CHCl_3$	Chloroform	61	$C_3H_6O_2$	Ethyl formate	54.1	C_3H_7Br	2-Bromopropane	59.4	61.97	79	5.3	15.7		195
1844	$CHCl_3$	Chloroform	61	$C_3H_6O_2$	Methyl acetate	57.1	C_3H_7Br	2-Bromopropane	59.4		Nonazeotrope				195
1845	$CHCl_3$	Chloroform	61	C_3H_7Br	2-Bromopropane	59.4	$C_4H_8O_2$	Isopropyl formate	68.8		Nonazeotrope				195
1846	$CHCl_3$	Chloroform	61	C_3H_8O	Isopropyl alcohol	82.3	C_4H_8O	2-Butanone	79.6		Nonazeotrope				334
1847	CH_2Cl_2	Dichloromethane	40.0	CH_4O	Methanol	64.7	$C_8H_{18}O_3$	2-(2-Butoxyethoxy)ethanol	230.6		Nonazeotrope				334
1848	CH_3NO_2	Nitromethane	101.2	C_6H_6	Benzene	80.1	C_6H_{12}	Cyclohexane	80.75		Nonazeotrope			v-l	343
1849 f	CH_4	Methane	-161.5	C_2H_6	Ethane	-88.6	C_3H_8	Propane	-44		Nonazeotrope			v-l	268
1850	CH_4O	Methanol	64.7	C_2H_6O	Ethyl alcohol	78.3	C_3H_6O	Acetone	56.1		Nonazeotrope			v-l	7
1851	CH_4O	Methanol	64.5	C_3H_6O	Acetone	56.1	$C_3H_6O_2$	Methyl acetate	56.3	53.7	17.4	5.8	76.8	v-l	335
1852	CH_4O	Methanol	64.5	C_3H_6O	Acetone	56.1	C_6H_{14}	Hexane	68.95	47	14.6	30.8	59.6		105
1853	CH_4O	Methanol	64.5	$C_3H_6O_2$	Methyl acetate	56.3	C_6H_{14}	Hexane	68.7	45	14	27	59		335

f $-200°$ to $50°$ F.

No.	A-Component Formula	A-Component Name	A B.P., °C	B-Component Formula	B-Component Name	B B.P., °C	C-Component Formula	C-Component Name	C B.P., °C	Azeo. B.P., °C	Comp. A	Comp. B	Comp. C		Ref.
1854	CH_4O	Methanol	64.7	$C_3H_9BO_3$	Trimethyl borate	68.7	C_4H_8O	Tetrahydrofuran	65		Nonazeotrope			v-1	115
1855	CH_4O	Methanol	64.7	C_6H_6	Benzene	80.1	C_6H_{12}	Cyclohexane	80.75		Nonazeotrope				223,362
1856[g]	C_2H_2	Acetylene	-84	C_2H_4	Ethylene	-104	C_2H_6	Ethane	-88		Nonazeotrope			v-1	137
1857	C_2H_3N	Acetonitrile	81.6	C_2H_6O	Ethyl alcohol	78.3	$C_6H_{15}N$	Triethylamine	89.7	70.1	34	8	58	v-1	335
1858	$C_2H_4Cl_2$	1,2-Dichloroethane	83.45	C_3H_6O	Acetone	56.4	C_6H_6	Benzene	80.1		Nonazeotrope			v-1	35
1859	$C_2H_4O_2$	Acetic acid	118.1	C_5H_5N	Pyridine	115.5	C_7H_{16}	Heptane	98.4	96.2	2	6.5	91.5		373
1859	$C_2H_4O_2$	Acetic acid	118.1	C_5H_5N	Pyridine	115.5	C_7H_{16}	Heptane	98.4	96.5	3.4	10.6	86.0		355
1860	$C_2H_4O_2$	Acetic acid	118.1	C_5H_5N	Pyridine	115.5	C_8H_{10}	Ethylbenzene	136.15	129.08	13.5	25.2	61.3		363
1861	$C_2H_4O_2$	Acetic acid	118.1	C_5H_5N	Pyridine	115.5	C_8H_{10}	o-Xylene	143.6	132.2	17.7	30.5	51.8		372
1862	$C_2H_4O_2$	Acetic acid	118.1	C_5H_5N	Pyridine	115.5	C_8H_{18}	Octane	125.75	115.7	10.4	20.1	69.5		355
1863	$C_2H_4O_2$	Acetic acid	118.1	C_5H_5N	Pyridine	115.5	C_9H_{20}	Nonane	150.7	128.0	20.7	29.4	49.9		372
1863	$C_2H_4O_2$	Acetic acid	118.1	C_5H_5N	Pyridine	115.5	C_9H_{20}	Nonane	150.7	128.0	20.9	29.3	49.8		355
1864	$C_2H_4O_2$	Acetic acid	118.1	C_5H_5N	Pyridine	115.5	$C_{10}H_{22}$	Decane	173.3	134.1	31.4	38.2	30.4		355
1865	$C_2H_4O_2$	Acetic acid	118.1	C_5H_5N	Pyridine	115.5	$C_{11}H_{24}$	Undecane	194.5	137.1	37.5	43.5	19.0		370
1866	$C_2H_4O_2$	Acetic acid	118.1	C_6H_7N	2-Picoline	134	C_8H_{18}	Octane	125.75	121.3	3.6	24.8	71.6		369
1867	$C_2H_4O_2$	Acetic acid	118.1	C_6H_7N	2-Picoline	134	C_9H_{20}	Nonane	150.7	135.0	12.9	38.4	48.8		369
1868	$C_2H_4O_2$	Acetic acid	118.1	C_6H_7N	2-Picoline	134	$C_{10}H_{22}$	Decane	173.3	141.3	19.9	46.8	33.3		369
1869	$C_2H_4O_2$	Acetic acid	118.1	C_6H_7N	2-Picoline	134	$C_{11}H_{24}$	Undecane	194.5	143.4	30.5	55.2	14.3		369
1870	$C_2H_4O_2$	Acetic acid	118.1	C_7H_9N	2,6-Lutidine	144	C_8H_{18}	Octane	125.75		Nonazeotrope				364
1871	$C_2H_4O_2$	Acetic acid	118.1	C_7H_9N	2,6-Lutidine	144	$C_{10}H_{22}$	Decane	173.3	147.0	12.6	74.3	13.1		323,364
1872	$C_2H_4O_2$	Acetic acid	118.1	C_7H_9N	2,6-Lutidine	144	C_8H_{18}	Octane	125.75		Nonazeotrope			v-1	358
1873	$C_2H_4O_2$	Acetic acid	118.1	C_8H_{10}	Ethyl-benzene	136.15	C_9H_{20}	Nonane	150.7	162.0	75.0	13.8	11.3		370
1874	$C_2H_5NO_2$	Nitroethane	114.2	$C_4H_8O_2$	p-Dioxane	101.3	$C_4H_{10}O$	Isobutyl alcohol	108	102.87	31.7	17.7	50.6		208
1875	C_2H_6O	Ethyl alcohol	78.3	C_6H_6	Benzene	80.1	C_6H_{12}	Methylcyclopentane	72	65.05	Nonazeotrope				304
1876	C_2H_6O	Ethyl alcohol	78.3	C_6H_6	Benzene	80.1	C_6H_{12}	Cyclohexane	80.75		30.4	10.8	58.8		362
1877	C_2H_6O	Ethyl alcohol	78.3	C_6H_6	Benzene	80.1	C_6H_{14}	Hexane	68.95		Nonazeotrope				326
1878	C_2H_6O	Ethyl alcohol	78.3	C_6H_6	Benzene	80.1	C_7H_{14}	Methylcyclohexane	100.88		Nonazeotrope				326

g -35°, 0°, 40° F.

TABLE II   TERNARY SYSTEMS   69

No.	A-Component Formula	Name	B.P., °C.	B-Component Formula	Name	B.P., °C.	C-Component Formula	Name	B.P., °C.	Azeotropic Data B.P., °C.	Composition, Wt.% A	B	C		Ref.
1879	C₂H₆O	Ethyl alcohol	78.3	C₆H₆	Benzene	80.1	C₇H₁₆	Heptane	98.4, 180-760 mm.		Nonazeotrope			v-l	240,339
1880	C₂H₆O	Ethyl alcohol "	78.3	C₆H₇N	Aniline	184.35	C₇H₈	Toluene	110.7	32.38	22.4	74.2	3.4	v-l	244
1881	C₂H₆O	Ethyl alcohol	78.3	C₆H₇N	Aniline	184.35	C₇H₁₆	Heptane	98.4		Nonazeotrope			v-l	138
1882	C₂H₆O	Ethyl alcohol	78.3	C₇H₈	Toluene	110.7	C₇H₁₆	Heptane	98.4		Nonazeotrope			v-l	138
1883	C₂H₆O₂	Ethylene glycol	196.7	C₇H₈O	o-Cresol	191	C₈H₁₁N	s-Collidine	171.30	189.65	33.6	62.4	4.0	v-l	188
1884	C₃H₄	Propadiene	-32	C₃H₄	Propyne	-23.2	C₃H₆	Propene	-47.7		Nonazeotrope				334
1885	C₃H₄	Propadiene	-32	C₃H₄	Propyne	-23.2	C₃H₈	Propane	-42.1		Nonazeotrope				334
1886	C₃H₄	Propadiene	-32	C₃H₄	Propyne	-23.2	C₄H₆	Butadiene	-4.5		Nonazeotrope				334
1887	C₃H₆O	Acetone	56.1	C₃H₆O₂	Methyl acetate	56.3	C₆H₁₄	Hexane	68.7	47	45	7	48		334
1888	C₃H₆O	Acetone	56.1	C₃H₈O	Isopropyl alcohol	82.3	C₅H₁₀O₂	Isopropyl acetate	88.7		Nonazeotrope				334
1889	C₃H₆O	Acetone	56.1	C₆H₅Cl	Chlorobenzene	131.8	C₆H₆	Benzene	80.1		Nonazeotrope			v-l	109
1890	C₃H₆O	Acetone	56.1	C₆H₆	Benzene	80.1	C₆H₁₂	Cyclohexane	80.75		Nonazeotrope			v-l	185
1891	C₃H₆O	Allyl alcohol	97.1	C₆H₁₄O	Isopropyl ether	68.3	C₉H₁₆O₂	2,2-Bis(allyloxy)propane	...		Nonazeotrope				334
1892	C₃H₆O₂	Propionic acid	140.7	C₅H₅N	Pyridine	115.5	C₁₁H₂₄	Undecane	194.5	147.1	55.5	26.4	18.1		370
1893	C₃H₈O	Isopropyl alcohol	82.3	C₄H₈O₂	Ethyl acetate	76.7	C₆H₁₂	Cyclohexane	80.7	68.3	···	···		v-l	334
1894	C₃H₈O	Isopropyl alcohol	82.3	C₅H₁₀O₂	Isopropyl acetate	88.7	C₆H₁₄O	Isopropyl ether	68.3		Nonazeotrope				334
1895	C₃H₈O	Isopropyl alcohol	82.3	C₆H₆	Benzene	80.1	C₆H₁₂	Cyclohexane	80.75		Azeotrope				209
1896	C₃H₈O	Propyl alcohol	97.25	C₆H₆	Benzene	80.1	C₆H₁₂	Cyclohexane	80.75 p.s.i.a. / 66.7-216.7	73.75	18	28	54	v-l	209,362 / 320
1897	C₃H₈O₂	2-Methoxyethanol	124.5	C₆H₆	Benzene	80.1	C₆H₁₂	Cyclohexane	80.75	73	9	39.1	51.9	v-l	331
1898[h]	C₃H₈O₂	2-Methoxyethanol	124.5	C₈H₈	Styrene	144	C₈H₁₀	Ethylbenzene	136.15		Nonazeotrope			v-l	152
1899	C₄H₈O	2-Butanone	79.6	C₆H₆	Benzene	80.1	C₆H₁₂	Cyclohexane	80.75 / 14.7-186.8 p.s.i.a.		Nonazeotrope			v-l	61,74 / 61,321

h 62 mm.

No.	A-Component Formula	A-Component Name	A-Component B.P., °C	B-Component Formula	B-Component Name	B-Component B.P., °C	C-Component Formula	C-Component Name	C-Component B.P., °C	Azeotropic Data B.P., °C	Composition, Wt.% A	B	C	Ref.
1900	$C_4H_8O_2$	Butyric acid	162.45	C_5H_5N	Pyridine	115.5	$C_{11}H_{24}$	Undecane	194.5		Nonazeotrope			370
1901	$C_4H_8O_2$	Ethyl acetate	77.05	C_6H_6	Benzene	80.1	C_6H_{12}	Cyclohexane	80.75	80.75	Nonazeotrope v-1			43,44
1902	$C_4H_9Cl_3Sn$	Butyltin trichloride	113/17	$C_8H_{18}Cl_2Sn$	Dibutyltin dichloride	157/17	$C_{12}H_{27}ClSn$	Tributyltin chloride	166/17		Nonazeotrope			334
1903	$C_4H_{10}O$	Isobutyl alcohol	107.0	C_6H_6	Benzene	80.1	C_6H_{12}	Cyclohexane	80.75	76.73	8	42	50	153,362
1904	$C_4H_{10}O$	Butyl alcohol	117.7	$C_4H_{11}N$	Butylamine	77.8	$C_8H_{19}N$	Dibutyl-amine	159.6		Nonazeotrope			334
1905	$C_4H_{10}O$	Butyl alcohol	117.75	C_5H_5N	Pyridine	115.5	C_7H_8	Toluene	110.7	108.7	11.9	20.7	67.4	140
1906	$C_4H_{10}O$	Butyl alcohol	117.75	C_6H_6	Benzene	80.1	C_6H_{12}	Cyclohexane	80.75	77.42	4	48	48	362
1907	$C_4H_{10}O$	Butyl alcohol	117.7	$C_6H_{12}O_2$	Butyl acetate	126.1	$C_8H_{18}O$	Butyl ether	142.1		Nonazeotrope			334
1908	$C_4H_{10}O_2$	2-Ethoxy-ethanol	135.1	C_8H_8	Styrene	145	C_8H_{10}	Ethyl-benzene	136.15, 5 mm.		Nonazeotrope v-1			110
					"				62 mm.		Nonazeotrope v-1			152
1909	$C_4H_{10}O_2$	2-Ethoxy-ethanol	135.1	C_8H_{10}	Ethyl-benzene	135.1	C_8H_{18}	Octane	125.75		Nonazeotrope v-1			227
1910	$C_5H_4O_2$	2-Furalde-hyde	161.7	C_6H_6	Benzene	80.1	C_6H_{12}	Cyclohexane	80.75		Nonazeotrope v-1			331
1911	$C_5H_4O_2$	2-Furalde-hyde	161.7	C_7H_8	Toluene	110.7	C_7H_{14}	Methylcyclo-hexane	101.1		Nonazeotrope v-1			114
1912	$C_5H_4O_2$	2-Furalde-hyde	161.7	C_7H_8	Toluene	110.7	C_7H_{16}	Heptane	98.4		Nonazeotrope v-1			114
1913	$C_5H_4O_2$	2-Furalde-hyde	161.7	C_7H_{14}	Methylcyclo-hexane	101.1	C_7H_{16}	Heptane	98.4		Nonazeotrope v-1			114
1914	C_5H_5N	Pyridine	115.5	$C_5H_{12}O$	Isoamyl alcohol	131	C_7H_8	Toluene	110.7	110.19	8.6	4.1	87.3	371
1915	C_5H_5N	Pyridine	115.5	C_8H_{10}	Ethyl-benzene	136.15	C_9H_{20}	Nonane	150.7		Nonazeotrope			363
1916	C_6H_6	Benzene	80.1	C_6H_{12}	Cyclohexane	80.75	$C_6H_{12}O$	4-Methyl-2-pentanone	115.9		Nonazeotrope v-1			65
1917	C_6H_6	Benzene	80.1	C_7H_{16}	2,3-Dimethyl-pentane	89.8	$C_{12}F_{27}N$	Perfluoro-tributyl-amine	...		Nonazeotrope v-1			190

TABLE I   BINARY SYSTEMS   71

No.	A-Component Formula	Name	B.P., °C.	B-Component Formula	Name	B.P., °C.	C-Component Formula	Name	B.P., °C.	Azeotropic Data B.P., °C.	Composition, Wt. % A	B	C		Ref.
1918[i]	C_6H_6O	Phenol	182	$C_6H_{10}O$	Cyclohexan-one	155.6	$C_6H_{12}O$	Cyclohexanol	160.65		Nonazeotrope			v-1	57
1919	C_6H_6O	Phenol	182	$C_6H_{10}O_4$	Ethylene diacetate	186	$C_8H_8O_2$	Phenyl acetate	195.7	194.45	26.4	34.4	39.2		253
1920	C_6H_7N	Aniline	184.35	$C_6H_{12}O$	Cyclohexanol	160.65	$C_6H_{13}N$	Cyclohexyl-amine	...		Nonazeotrope			v-1	242
1921[j]	C_6H_7N	Aniline	184.35	C_7H_8	Toluene	110.7	C_7H_{14}	Methylcyclo-hexane	101.1		Evaporation data				297
1922[k]	C_7H_7N	Aniline	184.35	C_7H_8	Toluene	110.7	C_7H_{16}	Heptane	98.4		Nonazeotrope			v-1	138
1923	$C_6H_{14}O_2$	Hexylene glycol	...	C_8H_{10}	Ethyl-benzene	136.15	C_8H_{16}	Ethylcyclo-hexane	131.8		Nonazeotrope			v-1	271
1924	C_7H_8O	$\underline{x}$-Cresol	202	C_7H_9N	Pyridine bases	143	$C_{10}H_8$	Naphthalene	218.1	202.48	81	9	10		367
1925	C_7H_8O	$\underline{x}$-Cresol	202	C_7H_9N	Pyridine bases	157	$C_{10}H_8$	Naphthalene	218.1	202.03	65.5	16.5	18		367
1926	C_7H_8O	$\underline{x}$-Cresol	202	C_7H_9N	Pyridine bases	163	$C_{10}H_8$	Naphthalene	218.1	202.39	62	17	21		367

[i] 90 mm.
[j] 80° to 100° C.
[k] 400 mm.

Table III. Quaternary Systems

No.		Formula	Name	B.P., °C.	B.P., °C.	Azeotropic Data — Azeotropic Composition				Ref.
						A	B	C	D	
1927	A	H_2O	Water	100	Nonazeotrope					334
	B	C_2H_3N	Acetonitrile	81.6						
	C	C_2H_6O	Ethyl alcohol	78.3						
	D	$C_6H_{15}N$	Triethylamine	89.7						
1928	A	H_2O	Water	100	70	8.7	11.1	0.1	80.1	84
	B	C_2H_6O	Ethyl alcohol	78.3						
	C	C_4H_6O	Crotonaldehyde	102.2						
	D	$C_4H_8O_2$	Ethyl acetate	77.1						
1929	A	H_2O	Water	100	62.19	7.1	17.4	21.5	54.0	357
	B	C_2H_6O	Ethyl alcohol	78.3	62.14	6.1	19.2	20.4	54.3	322,361
	C	C_6H_6	Benzene	80.1						
	D	C_6H_{12}	Cyclohexane	80.75						
1930	A	H_2O	Water	100	Nonazeotrope					326
	B	C_2H_6O	Ethyl alcohol	78.3						
	C	C_6H_6	Benzene	80.1						
	D	C_6H_{14}	Hexane	68.95						
1931	A	H_2O	Water	100	Nonazeotrope					326
	B	C_2H_6O	Ethyl alcohol	78.3						
	C	C_6H_6	Benzene	80.1						
	D	C_7H_{14}	Methylcyclohexane	100.88						
1932	A	H_2O	Water	100	64.79	6.8	18.7	62.4	12.1	325
	B	C_2H_6O	Ethyl alcohol	78.3						
	C	C_6H_6	Benzene	80.1						
	D	C_7H_{16}	Heptane	98.4						
1933	A	H_2O	Water	100	64.69	6.7	17.7	61.4	14.1	325
	B	C_2H_6O	Ethyl alcohol	78.3						
	C	C_6H_6	Benzene	80.1						
	D	C_8H_{18}	Iso-octane	...						

TABLE II TERNARY SYSTEMS 73

No.		Formula	Name	B.P., °C.	B.P., °C.	Azeotropic Composition				Ref.
						A	B	C	D	
1934	A	H_2O	Water	100	Min. b.p.					178
	B	C_3H_8O	Isopropyl alcohol	82.3						
	C	C_7H_8	Toluene	110.7						
	D	C_nH_{2n+2}	Paraffins	...						
1935	A	H_2O	Water	100	90.6	30	13	51	6	335
	B	$C_4H_{10}O$	Butyl alcohol	117.7						
	C	$C_6H_{12}O_2$	Butyl acetate	126.1						
	D	$C_8H_{18}O$	Butyl ether	142.1						
1936	A	$C_2H_4O_2$	Acetic acid	118.1	127.9	17	27	18	38	322,363
	B	C_5H_5N	Pyridine	115.5						
	C	C_8H_{10}	Ethylbenzene	136.15						
	D	C_9H_{20}	Nonane	150.7						
1937	A	$C_2H_4O_2$	Acetic acid	118.1	Nonazeotrope					372
	B	C_5H_5N	Pyridine	115.5						
	C	C_8H_{10}	o-Xylene	143.6						
	D	C_9H_{20}	Nonane	150.7						
1938	A	C_2H_6O	Ethyl alcohol	78.3	Nonazeotrope					v-1 304
	B	C_6H_6	Benzene	80.1						
	C	C_6H_{12}	Methylcyclopentane	72.0						
	D	C_6H_{14}	Hexane	68.95						
1939	A	C_2H_6O	Ethyl alcohol	78.3	Nonazeotrope					v-1 138
	B	C_6H_7N	Aniline	184.4						
	C	C_7H_8	Toluene	110.7						
	D	C_7H_{16}	Heptane	98.4						

Azeotropic Data

Formula Index

This index lists all compounds appearing in the azeotropic tables. Included are formula, name, standard boiling point, and numbers of the systems in which the compound appears as a component. The inorganic substances are indexed first.

Formula	Name and System Nos.
A	Argon B.p., -186 1, 2, 1675
$AsCl_3$	Arsenic chloride 3 B.p., 130
B_2H_6	Diborane B.p., -87.5 5
BeF_2	Beryllium fluoride 4
BrF_3	Bromine trifluoride 6-9 B.p., 135
BrF_5	Bromine pentafluoride 6, 10, 11
Br_2	Bromine B.p., 58.9 7, 12-20
Br_3P	Phosphorus tribromide 21 B.p., 175.3
CO	Carbon monoxide 1676 B.p., -192
CO_2	Carbon dioxide 22-26 B.p., -78.5
ClF_3	Chlorine trifluoride 27-29, 1677
ClH	Hydrogen chloride B.p., -85 27, 30-32, 1678
Cl_2	Chlorine B.p., -34.6 30, 33
Cl_2O_2S	Sulfuryl chloride 34-37 B.p., 69.1
Cl_3HSi	Trichlorosilane 38
Cl_3P	Phosphorus trichloride 39-44 B.p., 76
Cl_4Ge	Germanium chloride 3 B.p., 86.5
Cl_4Si	Silicon tetrachloride 45, 46 B.p., 57.6
Cl_4Sn	Tin chloride B.p., 114.1 47, 48
Cl_4Ti	Titanium tetrachloride 49-51 B.p., 146.2
DH	Deuterium hydride 52, 53
D_2	Deuterium B.p., -249.7 52, 54
FH	Hydrogen fluoride B.p., 19.4 8, 10, 12, 28, 33, 55-59, 1677, 1679
FNa	Sodium fluoride 4
F_5Sb	Antimony pentafluoride 55 B.p., 142.7
F_6U	Uranium hexafluoride B.p., 56 9, 11, 13, 29, 56, 1677

Formula	Name and System Nos.
F_6S	Sulfur hexafluoride 60
F_6W	Tungsten hexafluoride 61, 62 B.p., 19.5
HNO_3	Nitric acid B.p., 86 63, 64, 1680
H_2	Hydrogen B.p., -252.7 53, 54, 1676
H_2O	Water B.p., 100 31, 63, 65-522, 1679- 1832, 1927-1935
H_2O_2	Hydrogen peroxide 65 B.p., 151.4
H_2S	Hydrogen sulfide B.p., -59.6 22, 523, 524
H_2SO_4	Hydrogen sulfate 66
H_3N	Ammonia B.p., -33.4 525-529
H_4N_2	Hydrazine B.p., 113.8 67
He	Helium B.p., -268.9 530
N_2	Nitrogen B.p., -195.8 1675, 1676
N_2O	Nitrous oxide 23 B.p., -90.7
N_2O_5	Nitrogen pentoxide 68
O_2	Oxygen B.p., -183 1, 1675
O_2S	Sulfur dioxide B.p., -10 531, 1681
S	Sulfur B.p., 444.6 532
Se	Selenium B.p., 688 532
CCl_2F_2	Dichlorodifluoromethane B.p., -29.8 57, 533-539
CCl_3F	Trichlorofluoromethane B.p., 24.9 540, 541
CCl_4	Carbon tetrachloride B.p., 76.8 14, 34, 47, 542-556, 1833
CS_2	Carbon disulfide B.p., 46.2 69, 557-561
$CHClF_2$	Chlorodifluoromethane B.p., -40.8 58, 533, 562-567
$CHCl_2F$	Dichlorofluoromethane B.p., 7.63/723 mm. 568

Formula	Name and System Nos.	Formula	Name and System Nos.
$C_2H_5NO_2$	Nitroethane B.p., 114.0 84, 774-780, 1874	C_3H_4	Propyne B.p., -23.2 693, 924, 928-930, 1884-1886
C_2H_6	Ethane B.p., -88.6 26, 523, 603, 692, 727, 781, 1849, 1856	$C_3H_4Cl_4$	Tetrachloropropane 931
C_2H_6O	Ethyl alcohol B.p., 78.3 85, 547, 574, 593, 612, 681, 694, 702, 714, 744, 774, 782-866, 1686, 1692, 1699, 1703, 1707, 1709, 1712-1738, 1838, 1850, 1857, 1875-1882, 1927-1933, 1938, 1939	C_3H_4O	Acrolein B.p., 52.8 93
		C_3H_4O	2-Propyn-1-ol B.p., 115 94, 932, 1742, 1743
		$C_3H_4O_2$	Acrylic acid B.p., 141.2 95, 933, 1744
		$C_3H_4O_3$	Ethylene carbonate 96, 868
C_2H_6O	Methyl ether B.p., -23.7 531, 536, 612	C_3H_5Cl	3-Chloropropene 97, 934 B.p., 45.15
C_2H_6OS	Dimethylsulfoxide 867	C_3H_5Cl	x-Methylvinyl chloride 98
$C_2H_6O_2$	Ethylene glycol B.p., 197 86, 868-893, 1883	C_3H_5ClO	2-Chloro-2-propen-1-ol 935
C_2H_6S	Methyl sulfide B.p., 37.32 894-899	C_3H_5ClO	Epichlorohydrin 936 B.p., 116.45
$C_2H_6S_2$	Methyl disulfide 900-907 B.p., 109.44	$C_3H_5Cl_3$	1,2,3-Trichloropropane 936 B.p., 156.85
C_2H_7N	Dimethylamine B.p., 7.4 908, 1739	C_3H_5F	2-Fluoropropene 527 B.p., -23
C_2H_7N	Ethylamine B.p., 16.6 525, 909, 910	C_3H_5N	Propionitrile B.p., 97.4 923, 1741
C_2H_7NO	2-Aminoethanol B.p., 170.5 87, 911, 912	C_3H_5NO	Hydracrylonitrile 99 B.p., 229.7
$C_2H_8N_2$	1,1-Dimethylhydrazine 88	C_3H_6	Propene B.p., -48 925, 928, 937, 1884
$C_2H_8N_2$	Ethylenediamine B.p., 116 89, 913, 917, 1740	$C_3H_6Cl_2$	1,2-Dichloropropane B.p., 96.3 688, 730, 938, 939, 1745
$C_3Cl_3F_5$	1,2,2-Trichloropenta- fluoropropane B.p., 72.5 19	$C_3H_6Cl_2O$	2,3-Dichloro-1-propanol 100 B.p., 183.8
C_3F_6	Hexafluoropropene B.p., -6.1/2059 mm. 537, 564	C_3H_6O	Acetone B.p., 56.1 101, 548, 575, 594, 615, 683, 695, 703, 711, 717, 782, 911, 940-957, 1713, 1746- 1752, 1835, 1838- 1842, 1850, 1851, 1852, 1858, 1887-1890
C_3F_8	Perfluoropropane B.p., 12.5/6.064 atm. 565		
$C_3HF_5O_2$	Pentafluoropropionic acid 90, 918		
C_3HF_7	Heptafluoropropane B.p., 17/2328 mm. 538	C_3H_6O	Allyl alcohol B.p., 96.90 102, 549, 958-963, 1700, 1753-1755, 1891
$C_3H_2ClF_3O_2$	3-Chloro-2,2,3-trifluoro- propionic acid 919	C_3H_6O	Propionaldehyde B.p., 47.9 103, 964, 965, 1693
$C_3H_2F_4O_2$	2,2,3,3-Tetrafluoropro- pionic acid 920	C_3H_6O	Propylene oxide B.p., 38 104, 737, 938, 964, 966
		$C_3H_6O_2$	1,3-Dioxolane B.p., 75.6 105, 967-970
$C_3H_3ClF_3NO$	3-Chloro-2,2,3-trifluoro- propionamide 921	$C_3H_6O_2$	Ethyl formate B.p., 54.0 106, 577, 696, 704, 971, 1714, 1843
$C_3H_3F_4NO$	2,2,3,3-Tetrafluoropro- pionamide 922	$C_3H_6O_2$	Methoxyacetaldehyde B.p., 92/770 mm. 107
C_3H_3N	Acrylonitrile B.p., 77.2 91, 614, 716, 923, 1712, 1741	$C_3H_6O_2$	Methyl acetate B.p., 57.2 108, 576, 616, 697, 705, 972-1001, 1694, 1836, 1844, 1851, 1853, 1887
C_3H_3NS	Thiazole B.p., 116.8 92		
C_3H_4	Propadiene B.p., -32 526, 924-927, 1884- 1886		

Formula	Name and System Nos.	Formula	Name and System Nos.
$C_3H_6O_2$	Propionic acid B.p., 140.7 745, 1002-1010, 1756, 1892	C_3H_9ClSi	Chlorotrimethylsilane 590, 605
$C_3H_6O_3$	Methyl glycolate 1011, 1012 B.p., 151.2	C_3H_9N	Isopropylamine 1115 B.p., 32.4
$C_3H_6O_3$	s-Trioxane B.p., 114.5 1013	C_3H_9N	Propylamine B.p., 48.5 119
C_3H_7Br	2-Bromopropane B.p., 59.35 578, 971, 972, 1843-1845	C_3H_9N	Trimethylamine 120 B.p., 3.2
C_3H_7Cl	1-Chloropropane 109, 559 B.p., 46.6	C_3H_9NO	1-Amino-2-propanol B.p., 159.9 121, 1116-1119
C_3H_7Cl	2-Chloropropane 110, 934 B.p., 34.9	$C_3H_{10}N_2$	1,2-Propanediamine 1120-1122 B.p., 120.9
C_3H_7ClO	Propylene chlorohydrin B.p., 73/100 mm. 1014, 1745	$C_4Cl_3F_7$	2,2,3-Trichlorohepta- fluorobutane B.p., 97.4 1123-1125
C_3H_7NO	N,N-Dimethylformamide B.p., 153.0 111, 588, 718, 919-922, 1015	C_4F_8	Perfluorocyclobutane 539, 567
C_3H_7NO	Propionamide B.p., 222.1 1016-1018	$C_4HF_7O_2$	Perfluorobutyric acid B.p., 122.0 122, 1126-1128, 1679
$C_3H_7NO_2$	1-Nitropropane B.p., 131.6 112, 617, 783, 1019-1024	$C_4H_2O_3$	Maleic anhydride 1129, 1130
$C_3H_7NO_2$	2-Nitropropane B.p., 120.3 113, 618, 784, 1025-1030	C_4H_4	Vinylacetylene 1131
C_3H_8	Propane B.p., -42.1 524, 566, 604, 926, 929, 937, 1849, 1885	$C_4H_4O_2$	Diketene 941, 1132
C_3H_8O	Isopropyl alcohol B.p., 82.5 115, 595, 684, 731, 775, 785, 940, 958, 1019, 1025, 1031-1059, 1690, 1695, 1702, 1708, 1746, 1757-1766, 1846, 1888, 1893-1895, 1934	C_4H_4S	Thiophene B.p., 83.97 1133-1142
		C_4H_5Cl	2-Chloro-1,3-butadiene 1131, 1143, 1144
		C_4H_5N	3-Butenenitrile 123 B.p., 118.9
		C_4H_5N	Methacrylonitrile 124
		C_4H_6	1,3-Butadiene B.p., -4.5 676, 927, 930, 1886
C_3H_8O	Propyl alcohol B.p., 97.25 114, 550, 596, 746, 776, 1020, 1026, 1060-1072, 1701, 1767-1774, 1896	C_4H_6ClN	2-Chloro-2-methylpro- pionitrile B.p., 116 125
C_3H_8OS	2-(Methylthio)ethanol 1073	$C_4H_6Cl_2$	1,3-Dichloro-2-butene 1143
$C_3H_8O_2$	2-Methoxyethanol B.p., 124.5 116, 619, 1074-1094, 1775-1777, 1897, 1898	C_4H_6O	Crotonaldehyde B.p., 101.5 126, 1715, 1779, 1928
		C_4H_6O	Methacrylaldehyde 127 B.p., 68.0
$C_3H_8O_2$	Methylal B.p., 42.6 698, 706	C_4H_6O	3-Butene-2-one 1144
$C_3H_8O_2$	1,2-Propanediol B.p., 188 117, 939, 1095- 1106, 1778	$C_4H_6O_2$	2,3-Butanedione 1145 B.p., 90.7
$C_3H_8O_2$	1,3-Propanediol B.p., 214 118, 1107	$C_4H_6O_2$	3-Butenoic acid 128
C_3H_8S	Ethyl methyl sulfide 1108-1113 B.p., 66.61	$C_4H_6O_2$	Butyrolactone 131 B.p., 204.3
C_3H_8S	1-Propanethiol B.p., 67 1060, 1767	$C_4H_6O_2$	Crotonic acid B.p., 185 129, 130
$C_3H_9BO_3$	Trimethyl borate B.p., 68.7 620, 1114, 1854	$C_4H_6O_2$	Methyl acrylate 1696 B.p., 80.9
		$C_4H_6O_2$	Vinyl acetate B.p., 72.7 132, 621, 738, 942, 1031, 1146-1149, 1747
		$C_4H_6O_3$	Acetic anhydride B.p., 138 747, 1002, 1150-1152
		$C_4H_6O_3$	Propylene carbonate 133 B.p., 242.1

Formula	Name and System Nos.
C_4H_7Cl	1-Chloro-2-methylpropene 943 B.p., 68
C_4H_7ClO	2-Chloroethyl vinyl ether B.p., 109.1 134, 770, 1153
C_4H_7N	Butyronitrile B.p., 117.6 135
C_4H_7NO	2-Hydroxyisobutyronitrile 136
C_4H_8	1-Butene B.p., -6 677
C_4H_8	2-Methylpropene B.p., -6 674
$C_4H_8Cl_2O$	Bis(2-chloroethyl) ether B.p., 178.6 137, 732, 771, 869, 1154-1156
C_4H_8O	2-Butanone B.p., 79.6 138, 551, 579, 622, 689, 699, 707, 786, 944, 1145, 1157-1169, 1687, 1716, 1748, 1757, 1780- 1782, 1833, 1837, 1839, 1846, 1899
C_4H_8O	Butyraldehyde B.p., 75.7 139, 623, 787, 1170- 1176, 1717, 1749, 1783-1786
C_4H_8O	Ethyl vinyl ether B.p., 35.5 140, 739, 788, 1718
C_4H_8O	Isobutyraldehyde 141, 1170 B.p., 63.5
C_4H_8O	Methyl propenyl ether 142 B.p., 46.3
C_4H_8O	Tetrahydrofuran B.p., 66.1 624, 700, 708, 1114, 1854
C_4H_8OS	2-(Methylthio)propional- dehyde 143
C_4H_8OS	1,4-Oxathiane B.p., 149.2 144
$C_4H_8O_2$	Butyric acid B.p., 162.45 1171, 1177-1179, 1900
$C_4H_8O_2$	p-Dioxane B.p., 101 145, 748, 772, 789, 913, 1032, 1180-1184, 1874
$C_4H_8O_2$	Ethoxyacetaldehyde B.p., 105 146
$C_4H_8O_2$	Ethyl acetate B.p., 77.05 552, 560, 625, 690, 749, 790, 1033, 1061, 1185- 1191, 1893, 1901, 1928
$C_4H_8O_2$	2-Hydroxybutyraldehyde 147
$C_4H_8O_2$	Isobutyric acid B.p., 154.5 148, 1192-1194
$C_4H_8O_2$	Isopropyl formate B.p., 68.8 580, 1157, 1845
$C_4H_8O_2$	3-Methoxypropionaldehyde 149
$C_4H_8O_2$	2-Methyl-1,3-dioxolane 150 B.p., 82.5

Formula	Name and System Nos.
$C_4H_8O_2$	Methyl propionate B.p., 79.7 151, 626, 1034, 1697, 1756
$C_4H_8O_2$	Propyl formate B.p., 80.9 1195
$C_4H_8O_2$	2-Vinyloxyethanol 152, 870 B.p., 143
$C_4H_8O_3$	Ethylene glycol mono- acetate 871
C_4H_8S	Tetrahydrothiophene 1196-1202 B.p., 120.79
C_4H_9Cl	1-Chlorobutane B.p., 77.9 1203
C_4H_9Cl	1-Chloro-2-methylpropane 1035, 1158 B.p., 68.9
$C_4H_9Cl_3Sn$	Butyltin trichloride B.p., 113/17 mm. 1204, 1902
C_4H_9NO	N,N-Dimethylacetamide 750 B.p., 165
C_4H_9NO	Morpholine B.p., 128.3 153, 1206, 1207
$C_4H_9NO_2$	N-(2-Hydroxyethyl) acetamide 154
$C_4H_9NO_3$	2-Methyl-2-nitro-1- propanol 1208
C_4H_{10}	Butane B.p., -0.5 528, 679, 740, 743, 769
C_4H_{10}	2-Methylpropane 675, 1698 B.p., -11.70
$C_4H_{10}O$	Butyl alcohol B.p., 117.75 155, 553, 597, 627, 685, 751, 777, 791, 914, 1021, 1027, 1120, 1146, 1180, 1203, 1209-1231, 1787-1799, 1904-1907, 1935
$C_4H_{10}O$	sec-Butyl alcohol B.p., 99.5 156, 598, 778, 792, 1022, 1028, 1159, 1209, 1232-1237, 1787, 1800- 1807
$C_4H_{10}O$	tert-Butyl alcohol B.p., 82.41 599, 779, 1023, 1029, 1800
$C_4H_{10}O$	Ethyl ether B.p., 34.5 5, 157, 561, 581, 741, 966, 1036, 1211, 1239
$C_4H_{10}O$	Isobutyl alcohol B.p., 107 158, 600, 780, 915, 1024, 1030, 1121, 1172, 1181, 1185, 1210, 1238, 1783, 1808, 1874, 1903
$C_4H_{10}O_2$	1,4-Butanediol B.p., 230 1241
$C_4H_{10}O_2$	1,1-Dimethoxyethane 1173, 1784 B.p., 64.5
$C_4H_{10}O_2$	1,2-Dimethoxyethane 159, 1240 B.p., 85.2

Formula	Name and System Nos.
$C_4H_{10}O_2$	2-Ethoxyethanol B.p., 134.0 160, 793, 1186, 1242-1277, 1809, 1810, 1908, 1909
$C_4H_{10}O_3$	Diethylene glycol B.p., 245.5 161, 1154, 1278-1298
$C_4H_{10}S$	1-Butanethiol B.p., 98/770 mm. 1212, 1788
$C_4H_{10}S$	2-Butanethiol B.p., 85.15 1133, 1299
$C_4H_{10}S$	Ethyl sulfide B.p., 92.07 1300-1308
$C_4H_{10}S$	Isopropyl methyl sulfide B.p., 84.76 1134, 1299, 1309-1316
$C_4H_{10}S$	Methyl propyl sulfide 1317-1324 B.p., 95.47
$C_4H_{10}S_2$	Ethyl disulfide B.p., 154.11 1325, 1326
$C_4H_{11}N$	Butylamine B.p., 77.8 162, 794, 1037, 1213, 1719, 1758, 1789, 1811, 1904
$C_4H_{11}N$	Diethylamine B.p., 55.5 163, 628, 795, 909, 1327, 1328, 1704, 1812
$C_4H_{11}NO$	2-Dimethylaminoethanol B.p., 134.6 164, 908, 1739
$C_4H_{11}NO_2$	2,2'-Iminodiethanol 165, 910, 912, 1329
$C_5Cl_2F_6$	1,2-Dichlorohexafluoro- cyclopentene B.p., 90.6 1123, 1330
C_5F_{10}	Perfluorocyclopentane B.p., 25/833 mm. 61, 1331, 1332
C_5F_{12}	Perfluoropentane B.p., 40.86/1140 mm. 2, 60, 62, 1331
$C_5H_4F_8O$	2,2,3,3,4,4,5,5-Octafluoro- 1-pentanol 1333, 1334
$C_5H_4O_2$	2-Furaldehyde B.p., 162 166, 554, 1187, 1335-1339, 1910-1913
C_5H_5N	Pyridine B.p., 115.5 167, 589, 752, 1003, 1177, 1214, 1340-1349, 1678, 1689, 1813-1818, 1859-1865, 1892, 1900, 1905, 1914, 1915, 1936, 1937
$C_5H_6N_2$	2-Methylpyrazine 168 B.p., 133/737 mm.
C_5H_6O	2-Methylfuran B.p., 63 169, 965, 973, 1160
$C_5H_6O_2$	Furfuryl alcohol 1335
C_5H_6S	2-Methylthiophene B.p., 111.92 900, 1350-1353
C_5H_6S	3-Methylthiophene 1354-1360 B.p., 114.96

Formula	Name and System Nos.
C_5H_7ClO	2-Chloroallyl vinyl ether 935
C_5H_7N	3-Methyl-3-butenenitrile 170 B.p., 137
C_5H_8	Cyclopentene B.p., 44.4 974
C_5H_8	Isoprene B.p., 34.3 629, 1361-1365
C_5H_8	3-Methyl-1,2-butadiene 630 B.p., 40.8
C_5H_8	cis-1,3-Pentadiene 631 B.p., 44
C_5H_8	trans-1,3-Pentadiene 632 B.p., 42.0
$C_5H_8Cl_4$	Tetrachloropentane 931, 1366
C_5H_8O	Allyl vinyl ether 171, 959 B.p., 67.4
C_5H_8O	Cyclopentanone B.p., 130 172, 1367-1369
C_5H_8O	1-Methoxy-1,3-butadiene 173, 633 B.p., 90.7
C_5H_8O	3-Penten-2-one 174 B.p., 123.5
C_5H_8O	3-Methyl-3-buten-2-one 175 B.p., 97.9
C_5H_8O	4-Pentenal B.p., 106 176
$C_5H_8O_2$	Allyl acetate B.p., 104.1 177, 960
$C_5H_8O_2$	3,3-Dimethoxypropyne 1742 B.p., 111
$C_5H_8O_2$	Ethyl acrylate B.p., 99.5 178, 796, 933, 1370, 1720, 1744, 1819
$C_5H_8O_2$	Isopropenyl acetate B.p., 97.4 179, 945, 1150, 1373
$C_5H_8O_2$	Methyl methacrylate B.p., 100.8 180, 1215, 1242, 1371, 1372
$C_5H_8O_2$	2,4-Pentanedione (acetyl acetone) B.p., 140.6 181, 1373
$C_5H_8O_2$	Δ-Valerolactone 182
$C_5H_8O_2$	Vinyl propionate 183 B.p., 95.0
$C_5H_8O_3$	Methyl acetoacetate 1192 B.p., 171.7
C_5H_{10}	Cyclopentane B.p., 49.35 894, 975, 1374, 1375
C_5H_{10}	2-Methyl-1-butene B.p., 31.10 635, 797, 896, 1362
C_5H_{10}	3-Methyl-1-butene B.p., 21.2 634, 1361, 1376
C_5H_{10}	2-Methyl-2-butene B.p., 38.60 636, 895, 1363, 1377
C_5H_{10}	1-Pentene B.p., 29.92 637, 946, 976
C_5H_{10}	cis-2-Pentene B.p., 37.1 638
$C_5H_{10}Cl_2O_2$	Bis(2-chloroethoxy) methane B.p., 218.1 184

Formula	Name and System Nos.	Formula	Name and System Nos.
$C_5H_{10}N_2$	3-Dimethylaminopro- pionitrile B.p., 174.5 185	$C_5H_{12}N_2$	1-Methylpiperazine 206 B.p., 138.0
$C_5H_{10}O$	cis-1-Butenyl methyl ether B.p., 72.0 186, 1721	$C_5H_{12}O$	Active amyl alcohol B.p., 128.5 1333, 1367, 1398-1411
$C_5H_{10}O$	trans-1-Butenyl methyl ether B.p., 76.7 187	$C_5H_{12}O$	Amyl alcohol B.p., 137.9 643, 801, 1392- 1397, 1821
$C_5H_{10}O$	Ethyl isopropenyl ether 188 B.p., 61.9	$C_5H_{12}O$	Butyl methyl ether 802, 1724 B.p., 70.3
$C_5H_{10}O$	Isopropyl vinyl ether B.p., 55.7 189, 798, 1038	$C_5H_{12}O$	Isoamyl alcohol B.p., 131.85 1153, 1334, 1368,
$C_5H_{10}O$	3-Methyl-2-butanone 1378, 1379 B.p., 95.4		1398, 1412-1426, 1725, 1822, 1914
$C_5H_{10}O$	2-Pentanone B.p., 102.2 639, 799, 1039, 1380, 1820	$C_5H_{12}O$	2-Methyl-1-butanol B.p., 128.9 1369, 1427, 1428
$C_5H_{10}O$	3-Pentanone B.p., 102 1062, 1381-1384, 1768	$C_5H_{12}O$	2-Methyl-2-butanol 1429, 1430 B.p., 101.7
$C_5H_{10}O$	Propyl vinyl ether B.p., 65.1 190, 800, 1722	$C_5H_{12}O$	3-Pentanol B.p., 115.6 1341
$C_5H_{10}O$	Tetrahydropyran B.p., 88 191	$C_5H_{12}O_2$	1,2-Dimethoxypropane 207 B.p., 92
$C_5H_{10}O$	Valeraldehyde B.p., 103.3 192, 193	$C_5H_{12}O_2$	2,2-Dimethoxypropane 644, 803 B.p., 80
$C_5H_{10}OS$	2-Methylthioethyl vinyl ether 1073	$C_5H_{12}O_2$	1-Ethoxy-2-propanol 208 B.p., 132.2
$C_5H_{10}O_2$	Ethyl propionate 194 B.p., 99.1	$C_5H_{12}O_2$	3-Methoxy-1-butanol 209 B.p., 161.1
$C_5H_{10}O_2$	Isopropyl acetate B.p., 88.7 640, 753, 947, 1151, 1385, 1723, 1750, 1759, 1888, 1894	$C_5H_{12}O_2$	1,5-Pentanediol 210 B.p., 242.5
		$C_5H_{12}O_2$	2-Propoxyethanol 211 B.p., 151.5
		$C_5H_{12}O_3$	2-(2-Methoxyethoxy) ethanol B.p., 194.2 872, 1278, 1431-1454
$C_5H_{10}O_2$	3-Methoxybutyraldehyde 195 B.p., 131	$C_5H_{12}S$	Ethyl isopropyl sulfide 901 B.p., 107.22
$C_5H_{10}O_2$	Propyl acetate B.p., 101.6 196, 1063, 1243, 1769	$C_5H_{12}S$	3-Methyl-1-butanethiol 1412, 1822 B.p., 116
$C_5H_{10}O_2$	Valeric acid B.p., 187 197, 198, 1386	$C_5H_{13}N$	N-Methylbutylamine 212 B.p., 91.1
$C_5H_{10}O_2$	3-Vinyloxy-1-propanol 200, 1095, 1107	$C_5H_{13}NO$	1-Ethylamino-2-propanol 213 B.p., 159.4
$C_5H_{10}O_2$	1-Vinyloxy-2-propanol 199	$C_5H_{14}N_2$	N,N-Dimethyl-1,3-pro- panediamine B.p., 1349 214
$C_5H_{10}O_3$	3-Ethoxypropionic acid 201 B.p., 219.2	$C_6F_{12}O$	Perfluorocyclic ether 1455
$C_5H_{10}O_3$	3-Methoxybutyric acid 202	C_6F_{14}	Perfluorohexane 918, 1332, 1455, 1456, 1457
$C_5H_{10}O_3$	Methoxymethyl propionate 203	$C_6H_3Cl_3$	1,2,4-Trichlorobenzene 1458 B.p., 213
$C_5H_{11}N$	Piperidine B.p., 106 1340	$C_6H_4Cl_2$	o-Dichlorobenzene 1459, 1460 B.p., 179
$C_5H_{11}NO$	N,N-Dimethylpropion- amide B.p., 175.5 1004	C_6H_5Br	Bromobenzene B.p., 156.1 1461
$C_5H_{11}NO$	4-Methylmorpholine 204 B.p., 115.6	C_6H_5Cl	Chlorobenzene B.p., 131 1064, 1116, 1399, 1413, 1462, 1463, 1889
C_5H_{12}	2-Methylbutane B.p., 27.90 641, 897, 1364, 1376	C_6H_5F	Fluorobenzene B.p., 84.9 1464
C_5H_{12}	Pentane B.p., 36.15 205, 642, 719, 754, 898, 948, 977, 1365, 1377, 1387-1391	C_6H_5FO	o-Fluorophenol 1400, 1414
		$C_6H_5NO_2$	Nitrobenzene 1465 B.p., 210.85

Formula	Name and System Nos.
C_6H_{12}	trans-4-Methyl-2-pentene
	990 B.p., 58.4
C_6H_{12}	1,1,2-Trimethylcyclopro-
	pane B.p., 52.6
	952
$C_6H_{12}Cl_2O$	Bis(chloroisopropyl)ether
	239, 1014 B.p., 187.0
$C_6H_{12}Cl_2O_2$	1,2-Bis(2-chloroethoxy)
	ethane B.p., 240.9
	240
$C_6H_{12}O$	Butyl vinyl ether
	B.p., 94.2
	241, 652, 819,
	1218, 1790
$C_6H_{12}O$	Cyclohexanol B.p., 160.55
	242, 1461, 1482, 1490,
	1506, 1512, 1522, 1523,
	1825, 1918, 1920
$C_6H_{12}O$	2-Ethylbutyraldehyde
	243 B.p., 116.7
$C_6H_{12}O$	2-Hexanone B.p., 127.2
	1772
$C_6H_{12}O$	Hexanal B.p., 128.3
	245, 1219
$C_6H_{12}O$	Isobutyl vinyl ether
	B.p., 83.4
	244, 820, 1727
$C_6H_{12}O$	2-Methylvaleraldehyde
	B.p., 118.3
	246, 1067, 1773
$C_6H_{12}O$	4-Methyl-2-pentanone
	B.p., 116.2
	582, 653, 953, 1046,
	1468, 1513, 1524, 1525,
	1761, 1840, 1916
$C_6H_{12}OS$	2-Ethylthioethyl vinyl
	ether B.p., 169.7
	247
$C_6H_{12}O_2$	Butyl acetate B.p., 126.2
	583, 954, 1190, 1220,
	1232, 1244, 1526-1528,
	1785, 1791, 1826, 1827,
	1907, 1935
$C_6H_{12}O_2$	sec-Butyl acetate
	B.p., 112.3
	1233, 1526, 1802,
	1826, 1828, 1906
$C_6H_{12}O_2$	2-Ethylbutyric acid
	248 B.p., 194.2
$C_6H_{12}O_2$	2-Ethyl-2-methyl-1,3-
	dioxolane B.p., 117.6
	251
$C_6H_{12}O_2$	Hexanoic acid
	B.p., 205.15
	249, 1529, 1530
$C_6H_{12}O_2$	4-Hydroxy-4-methyl-2-
	pentanone (diacetone
	alcohol) B.p., 161
	250, 1508
$C_6H_{12}O_2$	2-Methylpentanoic acid
	252 B.p., 196.4
$C_6H_{12}O_2$	Tetrahydropyran-2-
	methanol B.p., 187.2
	254
$C_6H_{12}O_2$	4-Vinyloxy-1-butanol
	253, 1241
$C_6H_{12}O_2S$	2,4-Dimethylsulfolane
	1532, 1533

Formula	Name and System Nos.
$C_6H_{12}O_3$	2-Ethoxyethyl acetate
	B.p., 156.2
	255, 1534, 1829
$C_6H_{12}O_3$	Methyl 3-ethoxypropionate
	256
$C_6H_{12}O_3$	Paraldehyde B.p., 124
	821, 1499, 1535,
	1536, 1710, 1824
$C_6H_{12}O_3$	2-(2-Vinyloxyethoxy)-
	ethanol
	257, 1280
$C_6H_{13}Cl$	1-Chlorohexane
	258 B.p., 134.5
$C_6H_{13}N$	Cyclohexylamine
	B.p., 124.5
	259, 1491, 1514, 1920
$C_6H_{13}N$	Hexamethyleneimine
	260 B.p., 138
$C_6H_{13}NO$	N,N-Dimethylbutyramide
	B.p., 124.5/100 mm.
	1178
$C_6H_{13}NO$	2,6-Dimethylmorpholine
	261 B.p., 146.6
$C_6H_{13}NO$	4-Ethylmorpholine
	262 B.p., 138.3
$C_6H_{13}NO_2$	4-Morpholineethanol
	263 B.p., 225.5
C_6H_{14}	2,2-Dimethylbutane
	B.p., 49.74
	586, 654, 899,
	992, 1375
C_6H_{14}	2,3-Dimethylbutane
	B.p., 58.05
	955, 993, 1111, 1165
C_6H_{14}	Hexane B.p., 68.60
	40, 264, 657, 756, 822,
	956, 962, 994, 1005,
	1112, 1115, 1138, 1166,
	1175, 1195, 1221, 1456,
	1462, 1469, 1492, 1515,
	1520, 1537-1539, 1728,
	1753, 1782, 1786, 1792,
	1852, 1853, 1877, 1887,
	1930, 1938
C_6H_{14}	2-Methylpentane
	B.p., 60.27
	655, 823, 995
C_6H_{14}	3-Methylpentane
	565, 996 B.p., 63.28
$C_6H_{14}N_2$	2,5-Dimethylpiperazine
	B.p., 164
	265, 1245, 1394
$C_6H_{14}N_2O$	4-(2-Aminoethyl)morpho-
	line B.p., 204.7
	266
$C_6H_{14}N_2O$	1-Piperazineethanol
	267 B.p., 246.3
$C_6H_{14}O$	Isopropyl propyl ether
	1732
$C_6H_{14}O$	Butyl ethyl ether
	B.p., 92.2
	268, 658, 824,
	1729, 1762
$C_6H_{14}O$	2-Ethyl-1-butanol
	B.p., 147.0
	269, 1540, 1541
$C_6H_{14}O$	Ethyl isobutyl ether
	1730 B.p., 79

Formula	Name and System Nos.
$C_6H_{14}O$	Hexyl alcohol B.p., 157.85 270, 874, 1542, 1823
$C_6H_{14}O$	Isopropyl ether B.p., 68.0 271, 701, 709, 742, 757, 825, 963, 1152, 1183, 1327, 1370, 1543, 1705, 1731, 1751, 1763, 1812, 1819, 1830, 1841, 1891, 1894
$C_6H_{14}O$	2-Methyl-1-pentanol 272 B.p., 148
$C_6H_{14}O$	4-Methyl-2-pentanol 273, 1544 B.p., 131.8
$C_6H_{14}OS$	2-Butylthioethanol 1545
$C_6H_{14}O_2$	2-Butoxyethanol B.p., 171.2 1191, 1222, 1527, 1546-1557
$C_6H_{14}O_2$	1,1-Diethoxyethane 274 B.p., 102.1
$C_6H_{14}O_2$	1,2-Diethoxyethane 826, 1543 B.p., 121.1
$C_6H_{14}O_2$	1,1-Dimethoxybutane B.p., 114 275, 659, 1176
$C_6H_{14}O_2$	2,2-Dimethoxybutane 660 B.p., 106-7
$C_6H_{14}O_2$	1,3-Dimethoxybutane 276 B.p., 120.3
$C_6H_{14}O_2$	1,1-Dimethoxy-2-methyl- propane B.p., 104.7 277
$C_6H_{14}O_2$	Hexylene glycol 1558, 1559, 1923
$C_6H_{14}O_2$	2-Methyl-1,5-pentanediol 278 B.p., 242.4
$C_6H_{14}O_2$	3-Methyl-1,5-pentanediol 279 B.p., 248.4
$C_6H_{14}O_3$	Bis(2-methoxyethyl)ether 280 B.p., 162
$C_6H_{14}O_3$	Dipropylene glycol 1097, 1560, 1561
$C_6H_{14}O_3$	2-(2-Ethoxyethoxy)ethanol B.p., 202.8 281, 875, 1246, 1281, 1562, 1563
$C_6H_{14}O_4$	Triethylene glycol B.p., 288.7 1282, 1564-1568
$C_6H_{14}S$	Isopropyl sulfide 1196 B.p., 119.25
$C_6H_{15}N$	Diisopropylamine B.p., 84.1 282, 1047, 1764
$C_6H_{15}N$	1,3-Dimethylbutylamine 283 B.p., 108.5
$C_6H_{15}N$	Dipropylamine B.p., 109 284
$C_6H_{15}N$	N-Ethylbutylamine 285 B.p., 111.2
$C_6H_{15}N$	Hexylamine B.p., 132.7 286, 1048
$C_6H_{15}N$	Triethylamine B.p., 89.4 287, 827, 1706, 1830, 1857, 1927
$C_6H_{15}NO$	2-Butylaminoethanol 288 B.p., 199.3

Formula	Name and System Nos.
$C_6H_{15}NO$	2-Diethylaminoethanol 289, 1328 B.p., 162.1
$C_6H_{15}NO$	1-Isopropylamino-2-pro- panol B.p., 164.5 290
$C_6H_{15}NO_2$	1,1'-Iminodi-2-propanol B.p., 185/100 mm. 1117, 1569
$C_6H_{15}NO_3$	2,2',2''-Nitrilotriethanol 1329
$C_6H_{15}N_3$	4-(2-Aminoethyl)pipera- zine B.p., 222.0 291
$C_6H_{16}N_2$	N,N-Diethylethylenedi- amine B.p., 144.9 292
$C_6H_{16}N_2$	N,N,N',N'-Tetramethyl- ethylenediamine 293 B.p., 119
$C_6H_{16}OSi$	1-(Trimethylsiloxy)propane B.p., 100.3/735 mm. 1068
C_7F_{14}	Perfluoro(methylcyclo- hexane) B.p., 73-78 1470
C_7F_{16}	Perfluoroheptane B.p., 83 371, 1390, 1471, 1537, 1570-1573
C_7H_n	C_7 Hydrocarbons B.p., 95-120 1417, 1427
$C_7H_5F_3$	a,a,a-Trifluorotoluene 20 B.p., 103.9
$C_7H_6O_2$	Benzoic acid 1574
C_7H_7F	o-Fluorotoluene B.p., 114 1403, 1418
C_7H_8	Toluene B.p., 110.7 294, 556, 661, 828, 876, 902, 917, 967, 1049, 1069, 1098, 1118, 1122, 1132, 1184, 1197, 1223, 1342, 1404, 1419, 1428, 1430, 1493, 1516, 1521, 1534, 1538, 1575-1582, 1733, 1754, 1765, 1777, 1778, 1809, 1829, 1831, 1832, 1842, 1880, 1882, 1905, 1911, 1912, 1914, 1920, 1921, 1934, 1939
C_7H_8O	Benzyl alcohol B.p., 205.2 877, 1583
C_7H_8O	x-Cresol B.p., 202 1586-1588, 1924-1926
C_7H_8O	o-Cresol B.p., 191 878, 1585, 1883
C_7H_8O	m- and p-Cresol B.p., 202 1584, 1589, 1590
C_7H_8O	p-Cresol B.p., 201.7 1575, 1591
$C_7H_8O_2$	Guaiacol B.p., 205.0 295
C_7H_9ClO	2-Chloroallylidene di- acetate B.p., 212.1 296
C_7H_9N	2,6-Lutidine B.p., 144 297, 758, 1405, 1420, 1502, 1593, 1870-1872

Formula	Name and System Nos.	Formula	Name and System Nos.
C_7H_9N	N-Methylaniline 879, 1494, 1592	$C_7H_{14}O$	2,4-Dimethyl-3-pentanone 1406, 1421 B.p., 125
C_7H_9N	Pyridine bases 1586-1588, 1924-1926	$C_7H_{14}O$	3-Heptanone B.p., 147.6 307
C_7H_9N	Tetrahydrobenzonitrile 298 B.p., 195.1	$C_7H_{14}O$	4-Dimethyl-3-pentanone 308 B.p., 143.7
C_7H_9N	o-Toluidine B.p., 200.7 1594	$C_7H_{14}O$	5-Methyl-2-hexanone 309 B.p., 144
$C_7H_{10}O$	1,2,3,6-Tetrahydrobenzal- dehyde B.p., 164.2 299	$C_7H_{14}O_2$	Amyl acetate B.p., 146 310
$C_7H_{10}O_4$	Allylidene diacetate 300	$C_7H_{14}O_2$	Heptanoic acid 1597 B.p., 222.0
C_7H_{12}	2,4-Dimethyl-1,3-penta- diene B.p., 93.3 301	$C_7H_{14}O_3$	Ethyl 3-ethoxypropionate 311 B.p., 170.1
C_7H_{12}	1,3-Heptadiene 829	$C_7H_{14}O_3$	3-Methoxybutyl acetate 312 B.p., 171.3
C_7H_{12}	2,4-Heptadiene 830	$C_7H_{14}O_4$	2-(2-Methoxyethoxy)ethyl acetate B.p., 208.9 313
$C_7H_{12}Cl_4$	Tetrachloroheptane 1366	$C_7H_{15}N$	1,2-Dimethylpiperidine 1407, 1422 B.p., 128
$C_7H_{12}O$	3-Hepten-2-one 302, 1509 B.p., 162.9	$C_7H_{15}N$	2,6-Dimethylpiperidine B.p., 128
$C_7H_{12}O_2$	Butyl acrylate B.p., 147 303, 1224, 1793		1386, 1408, 1423
$C_7H_{12}O_2$	Cyclohexyl formate 1522	$C_7H_{15}NO$	N,N-Dimethylvaleramide B.p., 141/100 mm. 1386
$C_7H_{12}O_2$	2-Ethoxy-3,4-dihydro-1, 2-pyran B.p., 142.9 304	C_7H_{16}	2,2-Dimethylpentane B.p., 79.20 41, 839, 1113, 1316
$C_7H_{12}O_4$	Pimelic acid 305	C_7H_{16}	2,3-Dimethylpentane B.p., 89.78 42, 840, 1140, 1306, 1314, 1322, 1473, 1917
C_7H_{14}	1,1-Dimethylcyclopentane B.p., 87.85 831, 1303, 1312, 1320	C_7H_{16}	2,4-Dimethylpentane B.p., 80.50 43, 735, 841, 997, 1141, 1307, 1315, 1474, 1517
C_7H_{14}	cis-1,2-Dimethylcyclo- pentane B.p., 99.53 832	C_7H_{16}	3,3-Dimethylpentane 842 B.p., 86.07
C_7H_{14}	trans-1,2-Dimethylcyclo- pentane B.p., 91.87 833	C_7H_{16}	3-Ethylpentane 843 B.p., 93.47
C_7H_{14}	cis-1,3-Dimethylcyclo- pentane B.p., 91.73 834	C_7H_{16}	Heptane B.p., 98.25 314, 663, 722, 759, 844, 904, 957, 968, 998,
C_7H_{14}	trans-1,3-Dimethylcyclo- pentane B.p., 90.77 662, 835, 1139, 1302, 1311, 1319		1006, 1119, 1124, 1142, 1148, 1168, 1225, 1235, 1339, 1343, 1350, 1355, 1379, 1382, 1475, 1495,
C_7H_{14}	2,3-Dimethyl-1-pentene 836 B.p., 84.2		1518, 1570, 1577, 1595, 1598-1600, 1735, 1794,
C_7H_{14}	Ethylcyclopentane B.p., 103.47 837, 1317, 1354		1804, 1813, 1859, 1879, 1881, 1882, 1912, 1913, 1922, 1932, 1939
C_7H_{14}	trans-2-Heptene 1076 B.p., 98.0	C_7H_{16}	2-Methylhexane B.p., 90.05 664, 845, 999
C_7H_{14}	Methylcyclohexane B.p., 101.05 903, 1167, 1234, 1304, 1318, 1338, 1381, 1391, 1472, 1539, 1576, 1595, 1734, 1803, 1878, 1911, 1913, 1921, 1931	C_7H_{16}	3-Methylhexane B.p., 91.85 665, 846, 1000, 1305, 1313, 1321
C_7H_{14}	1,1,2,2-Tetramethylcyclo- propane B.p., 75.9 838	C_7H_{16}	2,2,3-Trimethylbutane B.p., 80.88 44, 666, 1001, 1519
$C_7H_{14}O$	Butyl isopropenyl ether 306 B.p., 114.8	$C_7H_{16}O$	3-Heptanol B.p., 156.4 1155
		$C_7H_{16}O$	5-Methyl-2-hexanol 315

Formula	Name and System Nos.
C₇H₁₆O₂	1-Butoxy-2-methoxyethane 316 B.p., 149.9
C₇H₁₆O₂	1-tert-Butoxy-2-methoxy-ethane 1077
C₇H₁₆O₂	1-Butoxy-2-propanol 317 B.p., 170.1
C₇H₁₆O₂	2-Ethyl-1,5-pentanediol 318 B.p., 253.3
C₇H₁₆O₂	Dipropoxymethane 1774 B.p., 146.6
C₇H₁₆O₃	Dipropylene glycol methyl ether 1601
C₇H₁₆O₃	1-(2-Ethoxyethoxy)-2-pro-panol B.p., 198.1 319
C₇H₁₆O₃	2-Ethoxyethyl 2-methoxy-ethyl ether 320
C₇H₁₆O₃	2-(2-Propoxyethoxy) ethanol B.p., 215.8 321
C₇H₁₇NO	1-Diethylamino-2-pro-panol B.p., 159.5 322
C₇H₁₈N₂	3-Diethylaminopropyl-amine B.p., 169.4 323
C₇H₁₈OSi	(Trimethylsiloxy)butane 1226
C₈F₁₆O	Perfluorocyclic oxide B.p., 102.6 1125, 1330, 1571, 1596, 1602-1604
C₈F₁₈O	Perfluorobutyl ether 1476, 1598 B.p., 100
C₈H₅Cl₃	ar-Trichlorostyrene 1605
C₈H₆Cl₂	ar-Dichlorostyrene 1431
C₈H₆O	Coumarone B.p., 173 1099
C₈H₇N	Indole B.p., 253 1283
C₈H₈	Styrene B.p., 67.9/57 324, 1070, 1078, 1247, 1606, 1736, 1898, 1908
C₈H₈Cl₂O₂	2-(2,4-Dichlorophenoxy) ethanol 325
C₈H₈O	Acetophenone B.p., 201.6 326
C₈H₈O	(Epoxyethyl)benzene 327 B.p., 194.2
C₈H₈O₂	Phenyl acetate B.p., 195.1 1483, 1919
C₈H₈O₃	Methyl salicylate 1608 B.p., 222.3
C₈H₁₀	Ethylbenzene B.p., 136.15 328, 1011, 1071, 1079, 1126, 1193, 1227, 1248, 1284, 1344, 1409, 1424, 1558, 1599, 1606, 1609-1614, 1860, 1873, 1898, 1908, 1915, 1923, 1936

Formula	Name and System Nos.
C₈H₁₀	m-Xylene B.p., 139 329, 728, 1012, 1127, 1129, 1194, 1249, 1535, 1607, 1615, 1616
C₈H₁₀	o-Xylene B.p., 143.1/735 mm. 760, 880, 1100, 1250, 1345, 1617, 1861, 1937
C₈H₁₀	p-Xylene B.p., 138.35 667, 729, 1072, 1080, 1128, 1251, 1285, 1536, 1618
C₈H₁₀O	α-Methylbenzyl alcohol 330 B.p., 203.4
C₈H₁₁N	N,N-Dimethylaniline B.p., 194.05 881, 1496, 1592
C₈H₁₁N	N-Ethylaniline 331 B.p., 204.8
C₈H₁₁N	α-Methylbenzylamine 332 B.p., 188.6
C₈H₁₁N	2-Methyl-5-ethylpyridine 333, 1578 B.p., 178.3
C₈H₁₁N	x-Methyl-1,2,3,6-tetra-hydrobenzonitrile 334 B.p., 205.4
C₈H₁₁N	s-Collidine B.p., 171.3 882, 1585, 1883
C₈H₁₂	4-Vinylcyclohexene 1081
C₈H₁₂O	2-Methyl-1,2,3,6-tetra-hydrobenzaldehyde 335 B.p., 176.4
C₈H₁₂O₂	3,4-Dihydro-2,5-dimethyl-2H-pyran-2-carboxalde-hyde B.p., 170.9 336
C₈H₁₂O₄	Diethyl fumarate 337 B.p., 218.1
C₈H₁₄	Diisobutylene B.p., 102.3 338, 1050, 1236, 1766, 1805
C₈H₁₄O	Bicyclo[2.2.1]-heptane-2-methanol B.p., 203.9 339
C₈H₁₄O	Cyclohexyl vinyl ether 1523
C₈H₁₄O	Diisobutylene oxide 340
C₈H₁₄O	2-Ethyl-2-hexenal 341, 668 B.p., 176
C₈H₁₄O	2-Octenal 342
C₈H₁₄O₂	Butyl methacrylate 1371
C₈H₁₄O₂	1,1-Diallyloxyethane 343 B.p., 150.9
C₈H₁₄O₂	2-Ethyl-3-hexenoic acid 344 B.p., 231.8
C₈H₁₄O₂	Vinyl 2-methylvalerate 345 B.p., 148.8
C₈H₁₄O₃	Bis(2-vinyloxyethyl)ether 346, 1619 B.p., 198.7
C₈H₁₄O₃	Butyl acetoacetate 347 B.p., 213.9
C₈H₁₄O₃	2-Ethoxyethyl methacryl-ate 1372

Formula	Name and System Nos.
$C_8H_{14}O_4$	Diethyl succinate 348　　　　　B.p., 216.2
$C_8H_{15}N$	2-(Aminoethyl)bicyclo [2.2.1]heptane 349　　　　　B.p., 185.9
C_8H_{16}	1,1-Dimethylcyclohexane 847　　　　　B.p., 119.54
C_8H_{16}	trans-1,2-Dimethylcyclo- hexane　　　B.p., 123.42 1051, 1252
C_8H_{16}	1,3-Dimethylcyclohexane 1383　　　　B.p., 120.3
C_8H_{16}	cis-1,3-Dimethylcyclohex- ane　　　　B.p., 120.09 1082
C_8H_{16}	trans-1,3-Dimethylcyclo- hexane　　　B.p., 124.45 849, 905, 1198, 1356
C_8H_{16}	cis-1,4-Dimethylcyclo- hexane　　　B.p., 124.32 848
C_8H_{16}	trans-1,4-Dimethylcyclo- hexane　　　B.p., 119.35 850
C_8H_{16}	Ethylcyclohexane 　　　　　　B.p., 131.85 1199, 1253, 1559, 1602, 1609, 1923
C_8H_{16}	1-Ethyl-1-methylcyclo- pentane　　　B.p., 121.52 851
C_8H_{16}	cis-1-Ethyl-2-methyl- cyclopentane 1052　　　　B.p., 128.05
C_8H_{16}	trans-1-Ethyl-2-methyl- cyclopentane B.p., 121.2 1053, 1083
C_8H_{16}	trans-1-Ethyl-3-methyl- cyclopentane B.p., 120.8 1054, 1084
C_8H_{16}	1-Octene　　　B.p., 121.6 1610
C_8H_{16}	cis-2-Octene　　B.p., 125.6 1254
C_8H_{16}	1,1,2-Trimethylcyclopen- tane　　　　B.p., 113.73 1055, 1357
C_8H_{16}	1,1,3-Trimethylcyclopen- tane　　　　B.p., 104.89 1056, 1085
C_8H_{16}	1,cis-2,cis-3-Trimethyl- cyclopentane B.p., 123.0 1086
C_8H_{16}	1,cis-2,trans-3-Trimethyl cyclopentane B.p., 117.5 852, 1057
C_8H_{16}	1,trans-2,cis-3-Trimethyl- cyclopentane B.p., 110.2 1087
C_8H_{16}	1,cis-2,trans-4-Trimethyl- cyclopentane 1058　　　　B.p., 116.73
C_8H_{16}	1,trans-2,cis-4-Trimethyl- cyclopentane 853　　　　　B.p., 109.29
C_8H_{16}	2,4,4-Trimethyl-1-pentene 493, 1088　B.p., 101.44

Formula	Name and System Nos.
C_8H_{16}	2,4,4-Trimethyl-2-pentene 854　　　　　B.p., 104.91
$C_8H_{16}O$	2-Ethylhexanal 350, 1540　　B.p., 163.6
$C_8H_{16}O$	2,4,4-Trimethyl-1,2- epoxypentane B.p., 140.9 351
$C_8H_{16}O$	2,4,4-Trimethyl-2,3- epoxypentane B.p., 127.3 352
$C_8H_{16}OS$	2-Butylthioethyl vinyl ether　　　　B.p., 210.5 353, 1545
$C_8H_{16}O_2$	2-Butoxyethyl vinyl ether 354
$C_8H_{16}O_2$	1,3-Dimethylbutyl acetate 1620　　　　B.p., 146.1
$C_8H_{16}O_2$	2,3-Epoxy-2-ethylhexanol 355
$C_8H_{16}O_2$	2-Ethylbutyl acetate 356, 1542　　B.p., 162.3
$C_8H_{16}O_2$	2-Ethylhexanoic acid 357, 1621　　B.p., 227.6
$C_8H_{16}O_2$	Hexyl acetate　B.p., 171.0 358
$C_8H_{16}O_2$	Iso-octanoic acid (iso- mers)　　　　B.p., 220 359
$C_8H_{16}O_2$	4-Methyl-2-pentyl acetate 　　　　　　B.p., 146.1 360, 1510, 1524, 1544
$C_8H_{16}O_2$	Octanoic acid　B.p., 238.5 1529, 1622
$C_8H_{16}O_3$	2-Butoxyethyl acetate 361　　　　　B.p., 192.2
$C_8H_{16}O_3$	2,5-Diethoxytetrahydro- furan　　　　B.p., 173.0 362
$C_8H_{16}O_3$	2-Ethoxyethyl 2-vinyloxy- ethyl ether　B.p., 194.0 363
$C_8H_{16}O_4$	2-(2-Ethoxyethoxy)ethyl acetate　　　B.p., 217.4 364, 1623
$C_8H_{17}Cl$	1-Chloro-2-ethylhexane 365　　　　　B.p., 173
$C_8H_{17}Cl$	3-(Chloromethyl)heptane 1541, 1624
$C_8H_{17}N$	N-Ethylcyclohexylamine 366　　　　　B.p., 164.9
$C_8H_{17}N$	5-Ethyl-2-methylpiperi- dine　　　　B.p., 163.4 367
$C_8H_{17}N$	ar-Methylcyclohexane- methylamine 368
$C_8H_{17}NO$	N,N-Dimethylhexanamide 1530
$C_8H_{17}NO$	4-Ethyl-2,6-dimethylmor- pholine　　　B.p., 158.1 369
C_8H_{18}	2,2-Dimethylhexane 　　　　　　B.p., 106.84 855, 1323, 1353
C_8H_{18}	2,3-Dimethylhexane 856, 906　　B.p., 115.61
C_8H_{18}	2,4-Dimethylhexane 1089　　　　B.p., 109.43

Formula	Name and System Nos.
C_8H_{18}	2,5-Dimethylhexane B.p., 109.15 1169, 1200, 1255, 1352, 1360, 1384
C_8H_{18}	3,3-Dimethylhexane 1256 B.p., 111.97
C_8H_{18}	3,4-Dimethylhexane 857 B.p., 117.73
C_8H_{18}	3-Ethyl-3-methylpentane 1257 B.p., 118.26
C_8H_{18}	Iso-octane 529, 1237, 1497, 1579, 1806, 1933
C_8H_{18}	2-Methylheptane B.p., 117.65 858, 907, 1201, 1351, 1359
C_8H_{18}	3-Methylheptane 859 B.p., 118.93
C_8H_{18}	4-Methylheptane 860 B.p., 117.71
C_8H_{18}	n-Octane B.p., 125.7 48, 370, 669, 723, 761, 1007, 1202, 1228, 1258, 1346, 1358, 1396, 1410, 1425, 1477, 1500, 1572, 1611, 1618, 1795, 1814, 1862, 1866, 1870
C_8H_{18}	2,2,3-Trimethylpentane 861, 1090 B.p., 109.84
C_8H_{18}	2,2,4-Trimethylpentane B.p., 99.24 862, 1059, 1308, 1324, 1478, 1580, 1600, 1603
C_8H_{18}	2,3,3-Trimethylpentane 863 B.p., 114.76
C_8H_{18}	2,3,4-Trimethylpentane 864 B.p., 113.47
$C_8H_{18}Cl_2Sn$	Dibutyltin dichloride B.p., 157/17 mm. 1204, 1625, 1902
$C_8H_{18}O$	Butyl ether B.p., 142.1 865, 883, 969, 1107, 1149, 1206, 1229, 1239, 1528, 1626, 1737, 1796, 1807, 1827, 1828, 1907, 1935
$C_8H_{18}O$	2-Ethyl-1-hexanol B.p., 184.8 371, 1156, 1484, 1615, 1624, 1626-1629
$C_8H_{18}O$	Iso-octyl alcohol (isomers) 372 B.p., 186.5
$C_8H_{18}O$	Octyl alcohol B.p., 195.15 1630
$C_8H_{18}OS$	2-Hexylthioethanol 1631
$C_8H_{18}O_2$	1-Butoxy-2-ethoxyethane 374 B.p., 164.2
$C_8H_{18}O_2$	1,1-Diethoxybutane 375 B.p., 146.3
$C_8H_{18}O_2$	5-Ethoxy-3-methylpen- tanol B.p., 211.7 376
$C_8H_{18}O_2$	2-Ethyl-1,3-hexanediol B.p., 243.1 373, 866, 1632, 1738

Formula	Name and System Nos.
$C_8H_{18}O_2$	2-Ethyl-3-methyl-1,5- pentanediol B.p., 265.5 377
$C_8H_{18}O_2$	2-Hexyloxyethanol 378 B.p., 208.1
$C_8H_{18}O_2$	2-(2-Methylpentoxy) ethanol B.p., 197.1 379
$C_8H_{18}O_3$	Bis(2-ethoxyethyl) ether B.p., 188.4 381, 1562, 1619
$C_8H_{18}O_3$	2-(2-Butoxyethoxy)ethanol B.p., 231.2 380, 884, 1286, 1479, 1633-1637, 1847
$C_8H_{18}O_4$	1,2-Bis(2-methoxyethoxy) ethane 382
$C_8H_{18}O_4$	2-[2-(2-Ethoxyethoxy) ethoxy]ethanol 1287
$C_8H_{19}N$	Dibutylamine B.p., 159.6 383, 1230, 1797, 1811, 1904
$C_8H_{19}N$	2-Ethylhexylamine 384 B.p., 169.1
$C_8H_{19}NO$	2-Diisopropylaminoethanol 385, 885 B.p., 190.9
$C_8H_{19}NO_2$	2,2'-Butyliminodiethanol 386
$C_8H_{19}NO_2$	1,1'-Ethyliminodi-2- propanol B.p., 238.9 387
$C_9F_{21}N$	Tris(perfluoropropyl) amine B.p., 130 1638
$C_9H_6N_2O_2$	2,4-Tolylene diisocyanate 1458, 1459, 1463, 1639
$C_9H_6N_2O_2$	2,6-Tolylene diisocyanate 1639
C_9H_7N	Isoquinoline 1640
C_9H_7N	Quinoline B.p., 237.3 1641
$C_9H_8O_2$	Vinyl benzoate 388
C_9H_{10}	α-Methylstyrene 1485
$C_9H_{10}O$	Benzyl vinyl ether 1583
$C_9H_{10}O_2$	1,2-Epoxy-3-phenoxypro- pane B.p., 244.4 389
$C_9H_{10}O_2$	Ethyl benzoate B.p., 213.3 584, 1584, 1591
$C_9H_{10}O_3$	Ethyl salicylate 1642 B.p., 233.7
$C_9H_{11}N$	5-Ethyl-2-vinylpyridine 390
C_9H_{12}	Cumene B.p., 152.4 391, 762, 1486, 1546, 1612, 1638, 1643
C_9H_{12}	m-Ethyltoluene 1433 B.p., 161.31
C_9H_{12}	o-Ethyltoluene B.p., 165.15 1259, 1434

Formula	Name and System Nos.	Formula	Name and System Nos.
C_9H_{12}	p-Ethyltoluene 1432 B.p., 161.99	C_9H_{20}	3,3-Diethylpentane 1266 B.p., 146.17
C_9H_{12}	x-Ethyltoluene 1531	C_9H_{20}	n-Nonane B.p., 150.2 403, 671, 724, 763, 970,
C_9H_{12}	Mesitylene B.p., 164.72 1260, 1437, 1644		1008, 1231, 1267, 1325, 1347, 1501, 1573, 1613,
C_9H_{12}	Propylbenzene 1487 B.p., 158.9		1617, 1627, 1648, 1798, 1815, 1863, 1867, 1873,
C_9H_{12}	1,2,3-Trimethylbenzene 1435 B.p., 176.08	C_9H_{20}	1936, 1937 2,2,3,3-Tetramethylpen-
C_9H_{12}	1,2,4-Trimethylbenzene B.p., 169.35		tane B.p., 140.27 1268
	1436, 1644	C_9H_{20}	2,2,3,4-Tetramethylpen-
$C_9H_{12}OS$	2-Benzylthioethanol 1645		tane B.p., 133.02 1092
$C_9H_{12}O_2$	Bicyclo[2.2.1]hept-5-ene- 2-ol acetate B.p., 188.6	C_9H_{20}	2,2,4,4-Tetramethylpen- tane B.p., 122.28
	392		1269
$C_9H_{13}NO$	5-Ethyl-2-pyridineethanol 393	C_9H_{20}	2,3,3,4-Tetramethylpen- tane B.p., 141.55
$C_9H_{14}O$	Isophorone B.p., 215.2 394, 1646		1270
$C_9H_{14}O$	1-Methyl-2,5-endomethyl-	C_9H_{20}	2,2,3-Trimethylhexane 1271 B.p., 133.60
	enecyclohexane-1-meth- anol B.p., 211.1	C_9H_{20}	2,2,4-Trimethylhexane 1272 B.p., 126.54
	395	C_9H_{20}	2,2,5-Trimethylhexane
$C_9H_{14}O$	Phorone B.p., 197.8 886		B.p., 124 1411, 1426, 1614
$C_9H_{14}OSi$	(Trimethylsiloxy)benzene 1488 B.p., 181.9	C_9H_{20}	2,3,3-Trimethylhexane 1273 B.p., 137.68
$C_9H_{15}N$	Triallylamine B.p., 151.1 396	C_9H_{20}	2,3,4-Trimethylhexane 1093, 1604 B.p., 139.0
C_9H_{16}	cis-Hexahydroindan 1547 B.p., 167.7	C_9H_{20}	2,3,5-Trimethylhexane B.p., 131.34
$C_9H_{16}O$	5-Ethyl-3-hepten-2-one 397 B.p., 193.5		1094, 1274
$C_9H_{16}O_2$	2,2-Bis(allyloxy)propane 1755, 1891	C_9H_{20}	2,4,4-Trimethylhexane 1275 B.p., 130.65
$C_9H_{16}O_4$	Dimethyl pimelate	C_9H_{20}	3,3,4-Trimethylhexane 1276 B.p., 140.46
	398 B.p., 248.9	$C_9H_{20}O$	2,6-Dimethyl-4-heptanol
C_9H_{18}	Butylcyclopentane 1261 B.p., 156.56		404, 1649 B.p., 178.1
C_9H_{18}	Isobutylcyclopentane 1262 B.p., 147.6	$C_9H_{20}O_2$	Dibutoxymethane 1799 B.p., 181.8
C_9H_{18}	Isopropylcyclohexane 1263 B.p., 154.5	$C_9H_{20}O_2$	Diisobutoxymethane 1808 B.p., 163.8
C_9H_{18}	1-Nonene B.p., 146.85 1264	$C_9H_{20}O_2$	2-Ethyl-2-butyl-1,3- propanediol
C_9H_{18}	Propylcyclohexane B.p., 156.72		405
	1265, 1647	$C_9H_{20}O_3$	1-(2-Butoxyethoxy)-2- propanol B.p., 230.3
C_9H_{18}	1,1,3-Trimethylcyclohex- ane B.p., 136.6		406
	1091	$C_9H_{20}O_3$	2-(2-Isoamyloxyethoxy) ethanol
$C_9H_{18}O$	2,6-Dimethyl-4-heptanone B.p., 169.4		1605
	399, 670, 1207,	$C_9H_{20}O_3$	2-Methoxymethyl-2,4-
	1511, 1525, 1620		dimethyl-1,5-pentanediol 407
$C_9H_{18}O$	2-Ethylheptanal 1616	$C_9H_{20}O_3$	1,1,3-Triethoxypropane 408
$C_9H_{18}O_2$	2-Heptyl acetate 400 B.p., 176.4	$C_9H_{20}O_4$	Tripropylene glycol 1650-1652
$C_9H_{18}O_2$	3-Heptyl acetate 401 B.p., 173.8	$C_9H_{21}N$	N-Methyldibutylamine 409 B.p., 163.1
$C_9H_{18}O_3$	3-(2-Ethylbutoxy)propionic acid	$C_9H_{21}N$	Tripropylamine B.p., 156. 410
	402	$C_9H_{21}NO_2$	1,1'-Isopropyliminodi-2-
$C_9H_{19}NO$	N,N-Dimethylheptanamide 1597		propanol B.p., 248.6 411

Formula	Name and System Nos.
$C_9H_{21}NO_3$	1,1',1''-Nitrilotri-2-pro-panol 1569
$C_9H_{21}NO_4$	2-(2-[2-(3-Aminopropoxy)ethoxy]ethoxy)ethanol 412
$C_{10}H_8$	Naphthalene B.p., 218.1 887, 1102, 1288, 1560, 1589, 1633, 1653, 1678, 1924-1926
$C_{10}H_8N_2$	2,2'-Dipyridyl B.p., 274. 1348
$C_{10}H_{10}O_4$	Dimethyl phthalate 413 B.p., 282.9
$C_{10}H_{12}O_3$	2-Phenoxyethyl acetate 414 B.p., 260.6
$C_{10}H_{14}$	Butylbenzene B.p., 183.27 1438, 1548
$C_{10}H_{14}$	sec-Butylbenzene B.p., 173.30 1439, 1549
$C_{10}H_{14}$	tert-Butylbenzene B.p., 169.11 1440, 1550
$C_{10}H_{14}$	p-Cymene B.p., 177.2 1445, 1498, 1551
$C_{10}H_{14}$	Dicyclopentadiene 415 B.p., 172
$C_{10}H_{14}$	m-Diethylbenzene 1442 B.p., 181.13
$C_{10}H_{14}$	p-Diethylbenzene 1443 B.p., 183.78
$C_{10}H_{14}$	5-Ethyl-m-xylene 1444 B.p., 183.75
$C_{10}H_{14}$	Isobutylbenzene 1441 B.p., 172.76
$C_{10}H_{14}$	1,2,3,5-Tetramethylben-zene B.p., 197.93 1446
$C_{10}H_{14}N_2$	Nicotine 416
$C_{10}H_{14}O_2$	Ethyl bicyclo[2.2.1]hept-5-en-2-carboxylate 417 B.p., 198
$C_{10}H_{14}O_3$	2-(2-Phenoxyethoxy)ethanol B.p., 297.9 418
$C_{10}H_{15}N$	N-Butylaniline B.p., 240.4 419
$C_{10}H_{15}N$	N-Ethyl-α-methylbenzyl-amine B.p., 201.2 420
$C_{10}H_{15}N$	N,N,α-Trimethylbenzyl-amine B.p., 195.8 421
$C_{10}H_{15}NO$	2-(α-Methylbenzylamino)ethanol 422
$C_{10}H_{16}$	Camphene 764
$C_{10}H_{16}O$	Dicyclopentenol 423
$C_{10}H_{16}O$	Trimethyltetrahydrobenz-aldehyde B.p., 204.5 424
$C_{10}H_{16}O_4$	Diisopropyl maleate 425 B.p., 228.7

Formula	Name and System Nos.
$C_{10}H_{18}$	Decahydronaphthalene 1654
$C_{10}H_{18}O_2$	Vinyl 2-ethylhexanoate 426 B.p., 185.2
$C_{10}H_{18}O_2$	Vinyl octanoate (isomers) 427
$C_{10}H_{18}O$	Menthone B.p., 209.5 1655
$C_{10}H_{20}$	n-Butylcyclohexane 1552 B.p., 180.95
$C_{10}H_{20}$	sec-Butylcyclohexane 1553 B.p., 179.3
$C_{10}H_{20}$	tert-Butylcyclohexane 1277 B.p., 171.5
$C_{10}H_{20}$	Isobutylcyclohexane 1554 B.p., 171.3
$C_{10}H_{20}$	cis-1-Isopropyl-4-methyl-cyclohexane B.p., 172.7 1555
$C_{10}H_{20}$	trans-1-Isopropyl-4-methylcyclohexane 1556 B.p., 170.5
$C_{10}H_{20}O$	2-Ethylhexyl vinyl ether 428, 1810 B.p., 177.7
$C_{10}H_{20}O$	Menthol 1655
$C_{10}H_{20}O$	Octyl vinyl ether 1630
$C_{10}H_{20}OS$	2-Hexylthioethyl vinyl ether 888, 1631
$C_{10}H_{20}O_2$	2-Ethylbutyl butyrate 429 B.p., 199.6
$C_{10}H_{20}O_2$	2-Ethylhexyl acetate 430, 1628 B.p., 198.4
$C_{10}H_{20}O_2$	4-Methyl-2-pentyl butyr-ate B.p., 182.6 431
$C_{10}H_{20}O_3$	2-Butoxyethyl 2-vinyloxy-ethyl ether B.p., 226.7 432
$C_{10}H_{21}Cl$	Chlorodecane (isomers) 433 B.p., 210.6
$C_{10}H_{21}N$	N-Butylcyclohexylamine 434 B.p., 209.5
$C_{10}H_{21}NO$	N,N-Dimethyloctanamide B.p., 187/100 mm. 1622
$C_{10}H_{22}$	Decane B.p., 173.3 672, 725, 765, 1009, 1016, 1349, 1593, 1654, 1816, 1864, 1868, 1871
$C_{10}H_{22}$	3-Ethyl-3-methylheptane 1326 B.p., 163
$C_{10}H_{22}$	3,3,5-Trimethylheptane 1557, 1656 B.p., 155.5
$C_{10}H_{22}$	Decyl alcohol B.p., 232.9 1581, 1657, 1831
$C_{10}H_{22}O$	2-Ethyloctanol 436 B.p., 220.5
$C_{10}H_{22}O$	2-Propylheptanol 437 B.p., 217.9
$C_{10}H_{22}OS$	2-(2-Ethylhexylthio)ethanol 1658
$C_{10}H_{22}O_2$	1,2-Dibutoxyethane 438 B.p., 203.6

Formula	Name and System Nos.
$C_{10}H_{22}O_2$	1,2-Diisobutoxyethane 439 B.p., 160.5
$C_{10}H_{22}O_3$	2-(2-Hexyloxyethoxy) ethanol B.p., 259.1 440
$C_{10}H_{22}O_4$	1,2-Bis(2-ethoxyethoxy) ethane B.p., 206.9 441
$C_{10}H_{22}O_4$	Tripropylene glycol methyl ether B.p., 243 889, 1103, 1659
$C_{10}H_{22}O_5$	Bis[2-(2-methoxyethoxy) ethyl]ether 442
$C_{10}H_{23}N$	Decylamine (isomers) 443 B.p., 203.7
$C_{10}H_{23}N$	Diamylamine (isomers) 444 B.p., 190
$C_{10}H_{23}N$	N,N-Dimethyl-2-ethylhex- ylamine B.p., 176.1 445
$C_{10}H_{23}NO$	2-Dibutylaminoethanol 446 B.p., 228.7
$C_{11}H_{10}$	1-Methylnaphthalene B.p., 244.8 1504, 1634, 1660
$C_{11}H_{10}$	2-Methylnaphthalene B.p., 241.1 773, 1447, 1505, 1561, 1563, 1590, 1601, 1608, 1621, 1623, 1635, 1640, 1641
$C_{11}H_{14}OS$	2-(Benzylmercapto)-ethyl vinyl ether 1289, 1645
$C_{11}H_{14}O_3$	Butyl salicylate 447 B.p., 268.2
$C_{11}H_{14}O_3$	Ethyl 6-formylbicyclo- [2.2.1]hept-5-en-2-car- boxylate 448
$C_{11}H_{16}$	tert-Amylbenzene 1448 B.p., 198.1
$C_{11}H_{16}O_3$	Allyl 6-methyl-3,4-epoxy- cyclohexanecarboxylate 449 B.p., 251.4
$C_{11}H_{17}N$	N,N-Diethyl-o-toluidine 1594
$C_{11}H_{18}O_2$	Isopropyl 6-methyl-3- cyclohexenecarboxylate 450 B.p., 215.2
$C_{11}H_{20}O$	5-Ethyl-3-nonen-2-one 451 B.p., 226.4
$C_{11}H_{20}O_4$	Diethyl pimelate 452 B.p., 268.1
$C_{11}H_{22}$	tert-Amylcyclohexane 1449 B.p., 198.1
$C_{11}H_{22}O$	5-Ethyl-2-nonanone 453 B.p., 222.9
$C_{11}H_{22}O_2$	2,6-Dimethyl-4-heptyl acetate B.p., 192.2 454
$C_{11}H_{22}O_3$	4-Methoxy-2,6-dipropyl- 1,3-dioxane B.p., 223.6 455
$C_{11}H_{24}$	Undecane B.p., 195.88 456, 673, 726, 766, 1010, 1017, 1179, 1450,

Formula	Name and System Nos.
	1817, 1865, 1869, 1872, 1892, 1900
$C_{11}H_{24}O$	5-Ethyl-2-nonanol B.p., 225 457, 1660, 1661
$C_{11}H_{24}O_2$	Diamyloxymethane 1397, 1821
$C_{11}H_{24}O_2$	2,2-Dibutoxypropane 458
$C_{11}H_{24}O_2$	2-Nonyloxyethanol 459 B.p., 225.5
$C_{11}H_{24}O_4$	1,1,3,3-Tetraethoxypro- pane B.p., 220.1 460
$C_{11}H_{25}N$	2-Ethyl-N-propylhexyl- amine 1629
$C_{11}H_{25}NO$	1-Dibutylamino-2-pro- panol B.p., 229.1 461
$C_{12}F_{27}N$	Tris(perfluorobutyl)amine B.p., 177 1457, 1643, 1647, 1648, 1656, 1917
$C_{12}H_9N$	Carbazole B.p., 294 1290, 1564, 1650, 1662, 1663
$C_{12}H_{10}$	Biphenyl B.p., 355.9 1291, 1664
$C_{12}H_{10}O$	Phenyl ether B.p., 259.3 890, 1292, 1565, 1574, 1642
$C_{12}H_{11}N$	Diphenylamine B.p., 265/350 mm. 1503
$C_{12}H_{14}O_4$	Diethyl phthalate 462 B.p., 294.3
$C_{12}H_{18}$	1,3,5-Triethylbenzene 1489 B.p., 215.5
$C_{12}H_{18}O$	Triisobutylene oxide 463
$C_{12}H_{19}N$	N-Butyl-α-methylbenzyl- amine B.p., 239.3 464
$C_{12}H_{20}O_2$	sec-Butyl 6-methyl-3- cyclohexenecarboxylate 465
$C_{12}H_{20}O_2$	Isobornyl acetate 767 B.p., 225.8
$C_{12}H_{20}O_4$	Dibutyl fumarate 466 B.p., 285.2
$C_{12}H_{20}O_4$	Dibutyl maleate 467 B.p., 280.6
$C_{12}H_{22}O_2$	2-Ethylhexyl crotonate 468 B.p., 241.2
$C_{12}H_{22}O_2$	Vinyl decanoate (isomers) 469
$C_{12}H_{22}O_4$	Diethyl 2-ethyl-3-methyl- glutarate B.p., 255.8 470
$C_{12}H_{23}N$	Dicyclohexylamine 471 B.p., 255.8
$C_{12}H_{24}$	2,6,8-Trimethylnonene 1649, 1665
$C_{12}H_{24}O$	2,6,8-Trimethyl-4-nona- none B.p., 218.2 472

Formula	Name and System Nos.	Formula	Name and System Nos.
$C_{17}H_{36}O$	3,9-Diethyl-6-tridecanol 510 B.p., 309	$C_{20}H_{36}O_4$	Bis(2-ethylhexyl)fumarate 514
$C_{17}H_{36}O$	x-Heptadecyl alcohol 1663, 1668, 1670	$C_{20}H_{36}O_4$	Bis(2-ethylhexyl)maleate 515
$C_{18}H_{24}N_2$	Bis(α-methylbenzyl)ethyl-enediamine 511	$C_{20}H_{40}O_3$	2-Ethylhexyl 3-(2-ethyl-hexyloxy)butyrate 516
$C_{18}H_{34}O_2$	Oleic acid 1672	$C_{20}H_{42}O$	Decyl ether (isomers) 517
$C_{18}H_{34}O_3$	Ricinoleic acid 1672	$C_{20}H_{42}O$	Eicosanol (isomers) 518
$C_{18}H_{36}O_2$	Stearic acid 1671, 1673	$C_{20}H_{43}N$	Didecylamine (isomers) 519
$C_{18}H_{38}O_2$	1,1-Bis(2-ethylhexyloxy) ethane 512	$C_{21}H_{38}O_3$	Allyl 9,10-epoxystearate 520
$C_{18}H_{39}NO$	2-[Bis(2-ethylhexyl)amino] ethanol 513	$C_{24}H_{38}O_4$	Dioctyl phthalate 1664
$C_{20}H_{30}O_2$	Abietic acid 1674	$C_{24}H_{52}O_4Si$	Tetra(2-ethylbutoxy)silane 521
		$C_{31}H_{58}O_6$	Tri(2-ethylhexyl)-1,2,4-butanetricarboxylate 522

Bibliography

1. Adelson and Evans, U. S. Patent 2,605,216 (1952).
2. Akers and Eubanks, Proc. Cryogenic Eng. Conf., 2nd, Boulder, 1957, p. 275; C.A. 52, 14267 (1958).
3. Albanesi, Pasquon, and Genoni, Chim. e ind. (Milan) 39, 814 (1957); C.A. 52, 3440 (1958).
4. Allen and Ellis, U. K. At. Energy Authority, IGR-R/CA, 216 (1957).
5. Alpert and Elving, Ind. Eng. Chem. 43, 1174, 1182 (1951).
6. Al'tshuler, Zviadadze, and Chizhikov, Zhur. Neorg. Khim. 2, 1581 (1957); C.A. 52, 7833 (1958).
7. Amer, Paxton, and Van Winkle, Ind. Eng. Chem. 48, 142 (1956).
8. Amick, Weiss, and Kirshenbaum, Ibid., 43, 969 (1951).
9. Ansul Chemical Co., Ansul Ethers, Chem. Prod. Bull.
10. Bachman and Simons, Ind. Eng. Chem. 44, 202 (1952).
11. Ballard and Van Winkle, Ibid., 45, 1803 (1953).
12. Banks and Musgrave, J. Chem. Soc. 1956, p. 4682; C.A. 51, 3216 (1957).
13. Barber and Cady, J. Am. Chem. Soc. 73, 4247 (1951).
14. Barr-David and Dodge, J. Chem. Eng. Data 4, 107 (1959).
15. Benning, U. S. Patent 2,641,579 (1953).
16. Bierlein, Univ. Microfilms (Ann Arbor, Mich.), No. 24,101; C.A. 52, 6909 (1958).
17. Bierlein and Kay, Ind. Eng. Chem. 45, 618 (1953).
18. Boublik and Kuchynka, Chem. Listy 50, 1181 (1956); C.A. 50, 16320 (1956); Collection Czechoslov. Chem. Communs. 21, 1634 (1956); C.A. 51, 11794 (1957).
19. Boublik and Kuchynka, Collection Czechoslov. Chem. Communs. 25, 579 (1960); C.A. 54, 16068 (1960).
20. Broich and Hunsmann, Ger. Patent 1,002,321 (1957); C.A. 53, 21663 (1959).
21. Brooks and Nixon, J. Am. Chem. Soc. 75, 480 (1953).
22. Brown and Smith, Australian J. Chem. 7, 264 (1954); 8, 62 (1955).
23. Ibid., 10, 423 (1957); C.A. 52, 3441 (1958).
24. Ibid., 12, 407 (1959); C.A. 54, 1003 (1960).
25. Ibid., 13, 30 (1960); C.A. 54, 10436 (1960).
26. Bruner and Darden, U. S. Patent 2,609,336 (1952).
27. Brzostowski, Malanowski, and Zieborak, Bull. acad. polon. sci., Classe III 7, 421 (1959); C.A. 54, 19067 (1960).
28. Burch and Leeds, Ind. Eng. Chem., Chem. & Eng. Data Ser. 2, 3 (1957).
29. Bures, Cano, and Wirth, J. Chem. Eng. Data 4, 199 (1959).
30. Burtle, Ind. Eng. Chem. 44, 1675 (1952).
31. Bushmakin and Kish, Zhur. Priklad. Khim. 30, 200 (1957); C.A. 51, 10989-90 (1957).
32. Butta, Chem. Listy 50, 1646 (1956); C.A. 51, 2349 (1957); Collection Czechoslov. Chem. Communs. 22, 1680 (1957); C.A. 52, 8708 (1958).
33. Byk and Sheherbak, Zhur. Fiz. Khim. 30, 56 (1956); C.A. 50, 10469 (1956).
34. Campbell and Hickman, J. Am. Chem. Soc. 75, 2879 (1953).
35. Canjar, Horni, and Rothfus, Ind. Eng. Chem. 48, 427 (1956).
36. Canjar and Lonergan, A.I.Ch.E. Journal 2, 280 (1956).
37. Carleton, Ind. Eng. Chem., Chem. & Eng. Data Ser. 1, 21 (1956).
38. Carswell and Morrill, Ind. Eng. Chem. 29, 1247 (1937).
39. Chabrier de la Saulniere, Ann. chim. 17, 353 (1942); C.A. 38, 3255 (1944).
40. Chaiyavech and Van Winkle, J. Chem. Eng. Data 4, 53 (1959).
41. Challis, U. S. Patent 2,691,624 (1954).
42. Chalov and Aleksandrova, Gidroliz. i Lesokhim. Prom. 10, 15 (1957); C.A. 51, 12585 (1957).
43. Chao, Univ. Microfilms (Ann Arbor, Mich.), No. 19076; C.A. 51, 9245 (1957).
44. Chao and Hougen, Chem. Eng. Sci. 7, 246 (1958); C.A. 52, 15219 (1958).
45. Choffe and Asselineau, Rev. inst. franç. pétrole et Ann. combustibles liquides 11, 948 (1956); C.A. 51, 3262 (1957).
46. Ibid., 12, 565 (1957); C.A. 51, 17383 (1957).
47. Choffe, Cliquet, and Meunier, Ibid., 15, 1051 (1960); C.A. 55, 8009 (1961).
48. Christian, J. Phys. Chem. 61, 1441 (1957).
49. Churchill, U. S. Patent 2,527,916 (1950).
50. Cines, Ibid., 2,692,227 (1954).
51. Ibid., 2,789,087 (1957).

52. Claxton, Physical & Azeotropic Data, Natl. Benzol & Allied Products Assoc. (1958).
53. Cole, Ind. Eng. Chem., Chem. & Eng. Data Ser. 3, 213 (1958).
54. Commercial Solvents Corp., Tech. Data Sheet No. 23 (1954).
55. Commercial Solvents Corp., unpublished data.
56. Conti, Othmer, and Gilmont, J. Chem. Eng. Data 5, 301 (1960).
57. Cova, Ibid., 5, 282 (1960).
58. Crawford, Edwards, and Lindsay, J. Chem. Soc. 1949, 1054; C.A. 43, 8835 (1949).
59. Crutzen, Jost, and Sieg, Z. Elektrochem. 61, 230 (1957); C.A. 51, 10214 (1957).
60. Curme and Johnson, "Glycols," ACS Monograph 114, Reinhold, New York, 1952.
61. Dakshinamurty and Rao, J. Appl. Chem. (London) 7, 654 (1957); C.A. 52, 6911 (1958).
62. Dakshinamurty and Rao, J. Sci. Ind. Research (India)15 B, 118 (1956); C.A. 50, 11753 (1956).
63. Ibid., 17B, 105 (1958); C.A. 52, 16851 (1958).
64. Dakshinamurty and Rao, Trans. Indian Inst. Chem. Engrs. 8, 57 (1955-6); C.A. 51, 14400 (1957).
65. Dakshinamurty, Rao, Acharya, and Rao, Chem. Eng. Sci. 9, 69 (1958); C.A. 53, 8727 (1959).
66. Dakshinamurty, Rao, Raghavacharya, and Rao, J. Sci. Ind. Research (India) 16B, 340 (1957); C.A. 52, 2485 (1958).
67. Davis and Evans, J. Chem. Eng. Data 5, 401 (1960).
68. Delzenne, Ind. Eng. Chem., Chem. & Eng. Data Ser. 3, 224 (1958).
69. Delzenne, J. Chem. Eng. Data 5, 413 (1960).
70. Desty and Fidler, Ind. Eng. Chem. 43, 905 (1951).
71. Din, Inst. intern. froid, Commissions intern. Zurich 1953, p. 17; C.A. 49, 5910 (1955).
72. Dobroserdov and Il'ino, Zhur. Priklad. Khim. 34, 386 (1961); C.A. 55, 13023 (1961).
73. Donald and Ridgeway, Chem. Eng. Sci. 5, 188 (1956).
74. Donald and Ridgeway, J. Appl. Chem. (London) 8, 403, 408 (1958); C.A. 53, 21109 (1959).
75. Donham, Univ. Microfilms (Ann Arbor, Mich.), Mic. 58-687; C.A. 52, 14267 (1958).
76. Dow Chemical Co., unpublished data.
77. Drake, Duvall, Jacobs, Thompson, and Sonnichsen, J. Am. Chem. Soc. 60, 73 (1958).
78. Drout, U. S. Patent 2,647,861 (1953).
79. Dunlap, Bedford, Woodbrey, and Furrow, J. Am. Chem. Soc. 81, 2927 (1959).
80. Dunn, U. S. Patent 2,524,899 (1950).
81. Du Pont, Polychemicals Dept. Sales Bull. (1959).
82. Du Pont, New Products Bull. No. 19.
83. Dykyj, Paulech, and Seprakova, Chem. Zvesti 14, 327 (1960); C.A. 54, 21908 (1960).
84. Eastman Chemical Products, Inc., unpublished data.
85. Ehrett and Weber, J. Chem. Eng. Data 4, 142 (1959).
86. Eiseman, J. Am. Chem. Soc. 79, 6087 (1957).
87. Eliot, U. S. Patent 2,635,072 (1953).
88. Eliot and Weaver, Ibid., 2,662,847 (1953).
89. Ellis, U. K. At. Energy Authority, Ind. Group Hdq. 5197 (1953); C.A. 53, 15681 (1959).
90. Ellis and Forest, Ibid., IGR-TN/CA 457 (1957); C.A. 51, 9245 (1957).
91. Ellis and Johnson, J. Inorg. & Nuclear Chem. 6, 194, 199 (1958).
92. Ellis and Razavipour, Chem. Eng. Sci. 11, 99 (1959); C.A. 54, 10436 (1960).
93. England, U. S. Patent 2,802,028 (1957).
94. Faerber, Ibid., 2,836,546 (1958).
95. Fahnoe, Ibid., 2,527,358 (1950).
96. Farbenwerke Hoechst, unpublished data.
97. Fastovskii and Petrovskii, Zhur. Fiz. Khim. 31, 836 (1957); C.A. 52, 25 (1958).
98. Feldman and Orchin, Ind. Eng. Chem. 44, 2909 (1952).
99. Feldman and Orchin, U. S. Patent 2,581,398 (1952).
100. Ibid., 2,590,096 (1952).
101. Fischer, Bingle, and Vogel, J. Am. Chem. Soc. 78, 902 (1956).
102. Fleischer, U. S. Patent 2,191,196 (1940).
103. Flom, Alpert, and Elving, Ind. Eng. Chem. 43, 1178 (1951).
104. Floyd, Univ. Microfilms (Ann Arbor, Mich.), No. 17,606; C.A. 51, 14352 (1957).
105. Forman, U. S. Patent 2,581,789 (1952).

106. Fowler, J. Soc. Chem. Ind. (London) 69, Suppl. 2, S65 (1950).
107. Fowler and Lim, J. Appl. Chem. (London) 6, 74 (1956); C.A. 53, 11924 (1959).
108. Fowler and Norris, Ibid., 5, 266 (1955).
109. Free and Hutchison, J. Chem. Eng. Data 4, 193 (1959).
110. Fried, Pick, Hala, and Vilim, Chem. Listy 50, 1039 (1956); C.A. 50, 16320 (1956); Collection Czechoslov. Chem. Communs. 21, 1535 (1956); C.A. 51, 11794 (1957).
111. Galaska-Krajewska, Bull. acad. polon. sci., Classe III 6, 257 (1958); C.A. 52, 15993 (1958).
112. Garber and Rabukhina, Zhur. Priklad. Khim. 33, 2782 (1960); C.A. 55, 9015 (1961).
113. Garber, Zelenevskaya, and Rabukhina, Ibid., 33, 694 (1960); C.A. 54, 20919 (1960).
114. Garner and Hall, J. Inst. Petrol. 41, 1, 18, 24 (1955).
115. Gause and Ernsberger, Ind. Eng. Chem., Chem. & Eng. Data Ser. 2, 28 (1957).
116. Gaziev, Zel'venskii, and Shalygin, Zhur. Priklad. Khim. 31, 1220 (1958); C.A. 52, 19361 (1958).
117. Gelperin and Novikova, J. Appl. Chem. U.S.S.R. 26, 841 (1953).
118. Gel'perin and Zelenetskii, Zhur. Fiz. Khim. 34, 2230 (1960); C.A. 55, 13022 (1961).
119. Goldberg and Zinov'ev, Zhur. Priklad. Khim. 33, 1913 (1960); C.A. 54, 23680 (1960).
120. Gondzik and Stateczny, Przemysl Chem. 9, 132 (1953); C.A. 48, 11759 (1954).
121. Gorodetskii, Morachevski, and Olevskii, Vestnik Leningrad Univ. 14, No. 22, Ser. Fiz. i Khim. No. 4, 136 (1959); C.A. 54, 8255 (1960).
122. Gorodetskii and Olevskii, Vestnik Leningrad Univ. 15, No. 16, Ser. Fiz. i Khim. No. 3, 102 (1960); C.A. 55, 1162 (1961).
123. Grekel, U. S. Patent 2,564,200 (1951).
124. Gropsianu, Kyri, and Gropsianu, Acad. rep. populare Romîne, Baza cercetări ştiint. Timisoara, Studii cercetări ştiint., Ser., ştiinte chim. 4, 73 (1957); C.A. 53, 19501 (1959); Gropsianu and Murarescu, Ibid., 3, 81 (1956); C.A. 51, 16028 (1957).
125. Hack and Van Winkle, Ind. Eng. Chem. 46, 2392 (1954).
126. Hahn, Brennstoff Chemie 35, 105 (1954).
127. Hamilton and Cogdell, U. S. Patent 2,831,902 (1958); C.A. 52, 14649 (1958).
128. Hanson, Hogan, Nelson, and Cines, Ind. Eng. Chem. 44, 604 (1952).
129. Hanson, Hogan, Ruehlen, and Cines, Chem. Eng. Prog. Symposium Ser. 49, No. 6, 37 (1953).
130. Harper and Moore, Ind. Eng. Chem. 49, 411 (1957).
131. Harrison and Somers, U. S. Patent 2,704,271 (1955).
132. Haughton, Chem. Eng. Sci. 4, 97 (1955).
133. Heitz, Am. J. Enol. Viticult. 11, 19 (1960); C.A. 54, 18007 (1960).
134. Hellwig and Van Winkle, Ind. Eng. Chem. 45, 624 (1953).
135. Hill and Van Winkle. Ibid., 44, 205, 208 (1952).
136. Hirata, Hirose, and Yanagawa, Kagaku Kogaku 24, 561 (1960); C.A. 54, 21908 (1960).
137. Hogan, Nelson, Hanson, and Cines, Ind. Eng. Chem. 47, 2210 (1955).
138. Hollo, Ember, Lengyel, and Wieg, Acta Chim. Acad. Sci. Hung. 13, 307 (1957); C.A. 52, 17862 (1958).
139. Hollo and Lengyel, Fette, Seifen, Anstrichmittel 62, 913 (1960); C.A. 55, 8009 (1961).
140. Hollo and Lengyel, Ind. Eng. Chem. 51, 957 (1959).
141. Hollo and Lengyel, Periodica Polytech. 2, 173 (1958); C.A. 53, 5799 (1959).
142. Hori, J. Agr. Chem. Soc. Japan 18, 155 (1942); C.A. 45, 4202 (1951).
143. Horyna, Collection Czechoslov. Chem. Communs. 24, 3253 (1959); C.A. 54, 10436 (1960).
144. Houser and Van Winkle, Ind. Eng. Chem., Chem. & Eng. Data Ser. 2, 12 (1957).
145. Hunt, U. S. Patent 2,862,856 (1958).
146. Ibl, Dandliker, and Trumpler, Chem. Eng. Sci. 5, 193 (1956).
147. Imperial Chemical Industries Ltd., unpublished data.
148. Ishiguro, Yagyu, Ikushima, and Nakazawa, J. Pharm. Soc. Japan 75, 434 (1955); C.A. 50, 2587 (1956).
149. Ishiguro, Yagyu, and Takagi, Yakugaku Zasshi 79, 1138 (1959); C.A. 54, 2857 (1960).
150. Ibid., 80, 30 (1960); C.A. 54, 11617 (1960).
151. Jakubicek, Collection Czechoslov. Chem. Communs. 26, 300 (1961); C.A. 55, 10026 (1961).
152. Jakubicek, Fried, and Vahala, Chem. Listy 51, 1422 (1957); C.A. 51, 17382 (1957).
153. Johannesen, U. S. Patent 2,656,389 (1953).

154. Johnson, Ward, and Furter, Can. J. Technol. 34, 514 (1957); C.A. 51, 14351 (1957).
155. Jordan, Univ. Microfilms (Ann Arbor, Mich.), Mic. 60-1188; C.A. 54, 14848 (1960).
156. Junghaus, J. prakt. Chem. [4]2, 265 (1955); C.A. 54, 17024 (1960).
157. Karr, Scheibel, Bowes, and Othmer, Ind. Eng. Chem. 43, 961 (1951).
158. Katz and Newman, Ibid., 48, 137 (1956).
159. Kay and Brice, Ibid., 45, 615 (1953).
160. Kay and Fisch, A.I.Ch.E. Journal 4, 293 (1958).
161. Kay and Rambosek, Ind. Eng. Chem. 45, 221 (1953).
162. Kay and Warzel, A.I.Ch.E. Journal 4, 296 (1958).
163. Keistler and Van Winkle, Ind. Eng. Chem. 44, 622 (1952).
164. Kenttamaa, Lindberg, and Nissema, Suomen Kemistilehti 33B, 189 (1960); C.A. 55, 8009 (1961).
165. Kharakhorin, Inzhener-Fiz. Zhur. Akad. Nauk Beloruss. S.S.R. 2, 55 (1959); C.A. 54, 1003 (1960).
166. Kibler and Gusakova, Gidroliz. i Lesokhim. Prom. 12, 14 (1959); C.A. 53, 12776 (1959).
167. Kieffer and Grabiel, Ind. Eng. Chem. 43, 973 (1951).
168. Kieffer and Holroyd, Ibid., 47, 457 (1955).
169. King, Kuck, and Frampton, J. Am. Oil Chemists' Assoc. 38, 19 (1961).
170. Kirk-Othmer, "Encyclopedia of Chemical Technology," Vol. III, p. 794, Interscience, New York, 1949.
171. Kirsanova and Byk, Zhur. Priklad. Khim. 31, 1610 (1958); C.A. 53, 2721 (1959).
172. Ibid., 33, 2784 (1960); C.A. 55, 9017 (1961).
173. Kobayashi, et al., Jap. Patent 3066 (1952); C.A. 48, 2772 (1954).
174. Kogan, Fridman, and Deizenrot, Zhur. Priklad. Khim. 30, 1339 (1957); C.A. 52, 2486 (1958).
175. Kogan, Fridman, and Romanova, Zhur. Fiz. Khim. 33, 1521 (1959); C.A. 54, 15993 (1960).
176. Kogan and Tolstova, Ibid., 33, 276 (1959); C.A. 53, 20995 (1959).
177. Kohoutek, Collection Czechoslov. Chem. Communs. 25, 288 (1960); C.A. 54, 16068 (1960).
178. Kominek-Szczepanik, Roczniki Chem. 33, 553 (1959); C.A. 53, 21723 (1959).
179. Korchemskaya, et al., Zhur. Priklad. Khim. 33, 2703 (1960); C.A. 55, 11006 (1961).
180. Kovalenko and Balandina, Uchenye Zapiski Rostov-a-Donu Univ. 41, 39 (1958); C.A. 55, 6118 (1961).
181. Kramer and Reid, J. Am. Chem. Soc. 43, 880 (1921).
182. Krichevskii, Khazanova, and Linshits, Zhur. Fiz. Khim. 31, 2711 (1957); C.A. 52, 8660 (1958).
183. Krishnamurty and Rao, J. Sci. Ind. Research (India) 14B, 55 (1955); C.A. 49, 11379 (1955).
184. Kurmanadharao, J. Sci. Ind. Research (India) 15B, 682 (1956); C.A. 51, 14352 (1957).
185. Kurmanadharao, Krishnamurty, and Venkatarao, Rec. trav. chim. 76, 769 (1957).
186. Kurmanadharao and Rao, Chem. Eng. Sci. 7, 97 (1957); C.A. 52, 15218 (1958).
187. Kurtyka, Bull acad. polon. sci. Classe III 2, 291 (1954); 3, 47 (1955).
188. Ibid., 4, 49 (1956); C.A. 51, 1676 (1957).
189. Kurtyka and Trabczynski, Roczniki Chem. 32, 623 (1958); C.A. 53, 2077 (1959).
190. Kyle and Tetlow, J. Chem. Eng. Data 5, 275 (1960).
191. Landwehr, Yerazunis, and Steinhauser, Chem. & Eng. Data Ser. 3, 231 (1958).
192. Lang, Z. physik. Chem. (Leipzig) 196, 278 (1950); C.A. 45, 10025 (1951).
193. Langer, Connell, and Wender, J. Org. Chem. 23, 50 (1958).
194. Latimer, A.I.Ch.E. Journal 3, 75 (1957).
195. Lelakowska, Bull. acad. polon. sci. Classe III 6, 645 (1958); C.A. 53, 6719 (1959).
196. Ledwock, Farbe u. Lack 62, 462 (1956).
197. Lessells and Corrigan, Ind. Eng. Chem., Chem. & Eng. Data Ser. 3, 43 (1958).
198. Lewis, U. S. Patent 2,641,580 (1953).
199. Lloyd and Wyatt, J. Chem. Soc. 1955, p. 2248.
200. Long, Martin, and Vogel, Chem. & Eng. Data Ser. 3, 28 (1958).
201. Lorette and Howard, J. Org. Chem. 25, 1814 (1960).
202. Lu, Can. J. Technol. 34, 468 (1957); C.A. 55, 8009 (1961).
203. Lumatainen, U. S. At. Energy Comm. ANL 6003 (1959); C.A. 54, 2858 (1960).
204. Lyvers and Van Winkle, Chem. & Eng. Data Ser. 3, 60 (1958).
205. Macarron, Rev. real acad. cienc. exact. fis. y nat. (Madrid) 53, 357, 607 (1959); C.A. 54, 16969 (1960).
206. MacWood and Paridon, J. Phys. Chem. 63, 1302 (1959).

207. Mair, Anal. Chem. 28, 52 (1956).
208. Malesinska and Malesinski, Bull Acad. polon. sci., Ser. sci. chim. 8, 191 (1960); C.A. 55, 11047 (1961).
209. Malesinski, Bull. acad. polon. sci., Classe III 4, 365 (1956); C.A. 51, 3217 (1957).
210. Maltese and Valentini, Chim. e ind. (Milan) 40, 548 (1958); C.A. 53, 798 (1959).
211. Malusov, Malafeev, and Zhavoronkov, Zhur. Fiz. Khim. 31, 699 (1957); C.A. 52, 25 (1958).
212. Markowska-Majewska, Bull. acad. polon. sci. Classe III 2, 291 (1954); C.A. 49, 2804 (1955).
213. Marks and Wingard, J. Chem. Eng. Data 5, 416 (1960).
214. Marschner and Burney, Ind. Eng. Chem. 44, 1406 (1952).
215. McCormack, Walkup, and Rush, J. Phys. Chem. 60, 826 (1956).
216. Melnikov and Tsirlin, J. Appl. Chem. U.S.S.R. 29, 1573; C.A. 51, 17377 (1957).
217. Melnikov and Tsirlin, Zhur. Fiz. Khim. 30, 2290 (1956); C.A. 51, 9245 (1957).
218. Metyushev, Trudy Tekhnol. Inst. Pishchevoi Prom. im. A. I. Mikoyana 15, 80 (1955); C.A. 51, 14398 (1957).
219. Metzger and Disteldorf, J. chim. phys. 50, 156 (1953).
220. Miller, Ind. Eng. Chem., Chem. & Eng. Data Ser. 3, 239 (1958).
221. Miller, J. Phys. Chem. 62, 512 (1958).
222. Minnesota Mining & Manufacturing Co., unpublished data.
223. Morachevskii and Komarova, Vestnik Leningrad. Univ. 12, No. 4, Ser. Fiz. i. Khim. No. 1, 118 (1957); C.A. 51, 11832 (1957).
224. Morachevskii and Leont'ev, Zhur. Fiz. Khim. 34, 2347 (1960); C.A. 55, 13023 (1961).
225. Morris and Snider, U. S. Patent 2,368,597 (1945).
226. Mukherjee and Grunwald, J. Phys. Chem. 62, 1311 (1958).
227. Murti and Van Winkle, A.I.Ch.E. Journal 3, 517 (1957).
228. Murti and Van Winkle, Ind. Eng. Chem., Chem. & Eng. Data Ser. 3, 72 (1958).
229. Myers, Ind. Eng. Chem. 47, 2215 (1955).
230. Ibid., 48, 1104 (1956).
231. Myers, Petrol. Refiner 36, 175 (1957).
232. Narinski, Kislorod 10, 9 (1957); C.A. 52, 13348 (1958).
233. Natradze and Novikova, Zhur. Fiz. Khim. 31, 227 (1957); C.A. 51, 15236 (1957).
234. Nelson, U. S. Patent 2,786, 804 (1957); C.A. 51, 11704 (1957).
235. Ibid., 2,839,452 (1958); C.A. 52, 15890 (1958).
236. Ibid., 2,922,753 (1960).
237. Newcome and Cady, J. Am. Chem. Soc. 78, 5216 (1956).
238. Newman, Bull inst. intern. froid. Annexe 1955, p. 390; C.A. 53, 15681 (1959).
239. Newman, Univ. Microfilms (Ann Arbor, Mich.) No. 16,290; C.A. 50, 12577 (1956).
240. Nielsen and Weber, J. Chem. Eng. Data 4, 145 (1959).
241. Nixon, U. S. Patent 2,604,439 (1952).
242. Novak, Matous, and Pick, Collection Czechoslov. Chem. Communs. 25, 2405 (1960); C.A. 55, 3170 (1961).
243. Nycander and Gabrielson, Acta Chem. Scand. 8, 1530 (1954); C.A. 49, 6678 (1955).
244. Oakeson and Weber, J. Chem. Eng. Data 5, 279 (1960).
245. Ocon and Espantoso, Anales real. soc. espan. fís. y quím. (Madrid) 54B, 401 (1958); C.A. 53, 1879 (1959).
246. Ocon, Espantoso, and Mato, Publs. inst. quím. fís. "Antonio de Gregorio Rocasolano" 10, 214 (1956); C.A. 51, 16028 (1957).
247. Ogawa, Kishida, and Kuyama, Kagaku Kogaku 22, 151 (1958); C.A. 52, 8661 (1958).
248. Ogorodnikov, Kogan, and Nemtsov, Zhur. Priklad. Khim. 33, 1599 (1960); C.A. 54, 21909 (1960).
249. Ogorodnikov, Kogan, and Nemtsov, J. Appl. Chem. U.S.S.R. 33, 2650 (1960); C.A. 55, 9017 (1961).
250. Olevskii and Golubev, Trudy Gosudarst. Nauk 1957, 42, 58; C.A. 53, 21107 (1959).
251. Orr and Coates, Ind. Eng. Chem. 52, 27 (1960).
252. Orszagh, Lelakowska, and Beldowicz, Bull. acad. polon. sci. Classe III 6, 419 (1958); C.A. 52, 19415 (1958).
253. Orszagh, Lelakowska, and Radecki, Ibid., 6, 605 (1958); C.A. 53, 6719 (1959).
254. Othmer, Chudgar, and Levy, Ind. Eng. Chem. 44, 1872 (1952).
255. Padgitt, U. S. Patent 2,531,361 (1950).
256. Palazzo, Univ. Microfilms (Ann Arbor, Mich.) Mic. 58-1354; C.A. 52, 13350 (1958).
257. Papousek and Smekal, Chem. Listy 52, 542 (1958); C.A. 52, 19391 (1958); Collection Czechoslov. Chem. Communs. 24, 2031 (1957).

258. Paquot and Perron, Bull. soc. chim. France 1957, p. 529; C.A. 51, 10156 (1957).
259. Patton, U. S. Patent 2,940,973 (1960).
260. Pennington, Ind. Eng. Chem. 44, 2397 (1952).
261. Pennington, private communication.
262. Peppel, Ind. Eng. Chem. 50, 767 (1958).
263. Perugini, Chim. e ind. (Milan) 39, 445 (1957); C.A. 51, 16028 (1957).
264. Pick, Hala, and Fried, Chem. Listy 52, 561 (1958); C.A. 52, 19393 (1958); Collection Czechoslov. Chem. Communs. 24, 1589 (1959).
265. Prausnitz and Targovnik, Chem. & Eng. Data Ser. 3, 234 (1958).
266. Politziner, Ibid., 2, 16 (1957).
267. Price and Hickman, Proc. West Va. Acad. Sci. 22, 69 (1952).
268. Price and Kobayashi, J. Chem. Eng. Data 4, 40 (1959).
269. Prill, U. S. Patent 2,599,482 (1952).
270. Pryanishinkov and Genin, J. Appl. Chem. U.S.S.R. 13, 140 (1940).
271. Qozati and Van Winkle, J. Chem. Eng. Data 5, 269 (1960).
272. Quintanilla, Riv. quím. ing. quím. Monterrey 2, 23 (1956); C.A. 51, 12585 (1957).
273. Rabe, Univ. Microfilms (Ann Arbor, Mich.), Mic. 58-1920; C.A. 52, 16853 (1958).
274. Rao, Rao, and Rao, J. Appl. Chem. (London) 7, 666 (1957); C.A. 52, 6909 (1958).
275. Rao, Sarma, Swami, and Rao, J. Sci. Ind. Research (India) 16B, 4 (1957); C.A. 51, 10196 (1957).
276. Rao, Swami, and Rao, A.I.Ch.E. Journal 3, 191 (1957).
277. Rao, Swami, and Rao, J. Sci. Ind. Research (India) 16B, 233 (1957); C.A. 51, 17301 (1957).
278. Ibid., p. 294; C.A. 52, 3440 (1958).
279. Ray, U. S. Patent 2,623,072 (1952).
280. Reed, Ibid., 2,511,993 (1950).
281. Reed, Univ. Microfilms (Ann Arbor, Mich.) No. 5338; C.A. 47, 11859 (1953).
282. Reed and Pennington, Modern Refrig. 53, 123 (1950).
283. Riddle, "Monomeric Acrylic Esters," p. 9, Reinhold, New York, 1954.
284. Ridley and Ridley, Brit. Patent 795,866 (1958); C.A. 53, 1154 (1959).
285. Rius, Otero, and Macarron, Chem. Eng. Sci. 10, 105 (1959); C.A. 53, 19501 (1959).
286. Rock and Shroder, Z. physik. Chem. (Frankfurt) [N.S.]11, 47 (1957).
287. Rohm and Haas, Tech. Data Sheet SP-148 (1958).
288. Rohrback and Cady, J. Am. Chem. Soc. 73, 4250 (1951).
289. Rose, Acciarri, and Williams, Chem. & Eng. Data Ser. 3, 210 (1958).
290. Rose, Papahronis, and Williams, Ibid., 3, 216 (1958).
291. Rossini, Mair, and Streiff, "Hydrocarbons from Petroleum," ACS Monograph 121, p. 89, Reinhold, New York, 1953.
292. Rowlinson, U. K. At. Energy Authority, Ind. Group R & DB(CA)TN-96D (1959); C.A. 53, 21114 (1959).
293. Rowlinson and Sutton, Proc. Roy. Soc. London A229, 396 (1955).
294. Rudakov and Kalinovskaya, Gidroliz i. Lesokhim. Prom. 10, 8 (1957); C.A. 51, 10989 (1957).
295. Ruhoff and Reid, J. Am. Chem. Soc. 59, 401 (1937).
296. Satapathy, Rao, Anjaneyulu, and Rao, J. Appl. Chem. (London) 6, 261 (1956); C.A. 51, 1677 (1957).
297. Schneider, Z. physik. Chem. (Frankfurt) [N.S.] 27, 171 (1961); C.A. 55, 13022 (1961).
298. Sebba, J. Chem. Soc. 1951, p. 1975.
299. Sense, Stone, and Filbert, U. S. At. Energy Comm. BMI-1186 (1957); C.A. 51, 15236 (1957).
300. Seryakov, Vaks, and Sidorina, Zhur. Obshchei Khim. 30, 2130 (1960); C.A. 55, 8009 (1961).
301. Shair and Schurig, Ind. Eng. Chem. 43, 1624 (1951).
302. Shakhparonov, et al., Zhur. Priklad. Khim. 33, 2699 (1960); C.A. 55, 11006 (1961).
303. Shcherbak, Byk, and Aerov, Ibid., 28, 1120 (1955); C.A. 50, 639 (1956).
304. Sinor and Weber, J. Chem. Eng. Data 5, 243 (1960).
305. Sizmann, Angew. Chem. 71, 243 (1959); C.A. 53, 15425 (1959).
306. Smirnova, Vestnik Leningrad Univ. 14, 80 (1959); C.A. 54, 8194 (1960).
307. Smirnova and Morachevskii, Zhur. Fiz. Khim. 34, 2546 (1960); C.A. 55, 6117 (1961).
308. Smirnova, Morachevskii, and Storonkin, Vestnik Leningrad Univ. 14, 70 (1959); C.A. 54, 9475 (1960).
309. Smit and Ruyter, Rec. trav. chim. 79, 1244 (1960); C.A. 55, 8008 (1961).
310. Smith and LaBonte, Ind. Eng. Chem. 44, 2740 (1952).
311. Spicer and Kruger, J. Am. Chem. Soc. 72, 1855 (1950).

312. Spicer and Meyer, Ibid., 73, 934 (1951).
313. Spicer and Page, Ibid., 75, 3603 (1953).
314. Steitz, U. S. Patent 2,552,911 (1951).
315. Storonkin and Markuzin, Vestnik Leningrad Univ. 13, 100 (1958); C.A. 52, 12493 (1958).
316. Storonkin and Morachevskii, Zhur. Fiz. Khim. 31, 42 (1957); C.A. 51, 15236 (1957).
317. Storonkin, Morachevskii, and Belousov, Vestnik Leningrad Univ. 13, 94 (1958); C.A. 52, 17863 (1958).
318. Studenberg and Thomas, Proc. S. Dakota Acad. Sci. 36, 167 (1957); C.A. 52, 15992 (1958).
319. Susarev, Zhur. Priklad. Khim. 34, 412 (1961); C.A. 55, 13023 (1961).
320. Swami and Rao, J. Sci. Ind. Research (India) 18B, 11 (1959); C.A. 53, 16628 (1959).
321. Swami, Rao, and Rao, J. Sci. Ind. Research (India) 15B, 550 (1956); C.A. 51, 6252 (1957); Trans. Indian Inst. Chem. Engrs. 9, 47 (1956-7); C.A. 53, 14622 (1959).
322. Swietoslawski, Bull. acad. polon. sci., Classe III 7, 13 (1959); C.A. 53, 19501 (1959).
323. Swietoslawski and Kreglewski, Ibid., 2, 77 (1954).
324. Swietoslawski and Malesinski, Ibid., 4, 159 (1956).
325. Swietoslawski and Zieborak, Bull. acad. polon. sci., Classe sci. math. et nat. Ser. A 1950, pp. 9, 13; C.A. 46, 410 (1952).
326. Swietoslawski, Zieborak, and Galska-Krajewska, Bull. acad. polon. sci., Classe III 7, 43 (1959); C.A. 54, 16068 (1960).
327. Swietoslawski and Zielenkiewicz, Bull. acad. polon. sci. 6, 111 (1958); C.A. 52, 15169 (1958).
328. Szapiro, Zeszyty Nauk Politech. Lodz. Chem. 7, 3 (1958); C.A. 52, 19475 (1958).
329. Tapp and Montagna, U. S. Patent 2,806,884 (1957).
330. Terry, Kepner, and Webb, J. Chem. Eng. Data 5, 403 (1960).
331. Thornton and Garner, J. Appl. Chem. (London) 1, S61, S68 (1951).
332. Trabczynski, Bull. acad. polon. sci., Classe III 6, 269 (1958); C.A. 52, 15993 (1958).
333. Tumova, Prenosil, and Pinkava, Chem. průmysl 8, 585 (1958); C.A. 54, 12702 (1960).
334. Union Carbide Chemicals Co., unpublished data.
335. Union Carbide Chemicals Co., "Glycols" (1958); "Alcohols" (1961).
336. Union Carbide Chemicals Co., Tech. Inform. Bull. (July 1959).
337. Urbancova, Chem. zvesti 13, 43 (1959); C.A. 53, 14621 (1959).
338. Vdovenko and Kovaleva, Zhur. Priklad. Khim. 31, 89 (1958); C.A. 52, 8661 (1958).
339. Wagner and Weber, Ind. Eng. Chem., Chem. & Eng. Data Ser. 3, 220 (1958).
340. Wang, Proc. Cryogenic Eng. Conf. 2nd, Boulder, 1957, p. 294; C.A. 52, 14267 (1958).
341. Watanabe and Conlon, U. S. Patent 2,760,990 (1956); C.A. 51, 3654 (1957).
342. Weber, Ind. Eng. Chem. 48, 134 (1956).
343. Weck and Hunt, Ibid., 46, 2521 (1954).
344. Wehe and Coates, A.I.Ch.E. Journal 1, 241 (1955).
345. Weismann and Wood, J. Chem. Phys. 32, 1153 (1960).
346. Whipple, Ind. Eng. Chem. 44, 1664 (1952).
347. Wilson and Simons, Ibid., 44, 2214 (1952).
348. Wingard and Durant, J. Alabama Acad. Sci. 27, 11 (1955); C.A. 50, 10469 (1956).
349. Wingard, Durant, Tubbs, and Brown, Ind. Eng. Chem. 47, 1757 (1955).
350. Wingard and Piazza, Alabama Polytech. Inst. Eng. Expt. Sta. Bull. No. 32 (1958); C.A. 53, 12776 (1959).
351. Wyandotte Chemical Corp., Market Development Property Sheet (Feb. 25, 1955).
352. Yamamoto and Maruyama, Kagaku Kogaku 23, 635 (1959); C.A. 54, 1004 (1960).
353. Yates and Kelly, U. S. Patent 2,752,295 (1956).
354. Yen and Reed, J. Chem. Eng. Data 4, 102 (1959).
355. Zieborak, Bull. acad. polon sci., Classe III 3, 531 (1955).
356. Ibid., 6, 443, 449 (1958); C.A. 52, 19392 (1958).
357. Zieborak, Bull. intern. polon. sci., Classe sci., math., et nat. Ser. A 1950, p. 15; C.A. 46, 410 (1952).
358. Zieborak and Brzostowski, Bull. acad. polon. sci., Classe III 5, 309 (1957); C.A. 51, 14399 (1957).
359. Ibid., 6, 169 (1958); C.A. 52, 13349 (1958).

360. Zieborak, Brzostowski, and Kaminski, Ibid., 6, 371 (1958); C.A. 52, 19393 (1958).
361. Zieborak and Galska, Ibid., 3, 383 (1955); C.A. 50, 9080 (1956).
362. Zieborak and Galska-Krajewska, Ibid., 6, 763 (1958); C.A. 53, 12777 (1959).
363. Ibid., 7, 253 (1959); C.A. 54, 16068 (1960).
364. Zieborak, Kaczorowana-Badyoczek, and Maczynska, Roczniki Chem. 29, 783 (1955); C.A. 50, 6119 (1956).
365. Zieborak, Maczynska, and Maczynski, Ibid., 32, 85 (1958); C.A. 52, 12493 (1958).
366. Ibid., p. 295; C.A. 52, 17862 (1958).
367. Zieborak and Markowska-Majewska, Bull. acad. polon. sci., Classe III 2, 341 (1954).
368. Zieborak and Olszewski, Ibid., 4, 823 (1956); C.A. 51, 7789 (1957).
369. Zieborak and Wyrzykowska-Stankiewicz, Ibid., 6, 377 (1958); C.A. 52, 19392 (1958).
370. Ibid., p. 517; C.A. 53, 3875 (1959).
371. Ibid., 8, 137 (1960); C.A. 55, 11047 (1961).
372. Ibid., 7, 247 (1959); C.A. 54, 16068 (1960).
373. Zieborak and Zieborak, Ibid., 2, 287 (1954); C.A. 49, 2803 (1955).
374. Zilberman, J. Appl. Chem. U.S.S.R. 26, 809 (1954).